'**A man could burn up for you,**'
Michael said softly, '**and you
wouldn't even smell the cinders.**'

'You're crazy,' Alexis said, shaken.

'Am I?' He gave a half-laugh. 'Maybe you're
right.'

He pulled her against him so that her hand was
caught between their bodies. His skin under her
fingers was smooth and tingling with warmth.
Alexis gasped. He bent his head so that his
mouth was just a breath away...

Dear Reader

A new year is starting and now is the time to think about the kind of stories you've enjoyed reading during the past year and the stories you would like to read throughout this coming year. As Valentine's Day approaches, why not dream up the most perfect romantic evening for yourself? No doubt it will include a sprinkling of charm, a good degree of atmosphere, a healthy amount of passion and love, and of course your favourite Mills & Boon novel. Keep romance close to your heart—make this year special!

The Editor

Born in London, **Sophie Weston** is a traveller by nature who started writing when she was five. She wrote her first romance recovering from illness, thinking her travelling was over. She was wrong, but she enjoyed it so much that she has carried on. These days she lives in the heart of the city with two demanding cats and a cherry tree—and travels the world looking for settings for her stories.

Recent titles by the same author:

GOBLIN COURT
NO PROVOCATION
HABIT OF COMMAND

DANCE WITH ME

BY

SOPHIE WESTON

MILLS & BOON LIMITED
ETON HOUSE   18-24 PARADISE ROAD
RICHMOND   SURREY   TW9 1SR

First published in Great Britain 1992
by Mills & Boon Limited

© *Sophie Weston 1992*

Australian copyright 1992
Philippine copyright 1993
This edition 1993

ISBN 0 263 77899 1

Set in Times Roman 10 on 11¼ pt.
01-9302-52046 C

Made and printed in Great Britain

CHAPTER ONE

THE moment Alexis arrived, she knew she had made a mistake.

The room was crowded. She had been afraid that her concert clothes—slim black skirt and long-sleeved white blouse—would be too formal. In fact it left her underdressed, she thought wryly. With her long red hair caught severely in at the nape of the neck, she looked like the maid, among all the bared shoulders and the diamonds.

'Hell,' she said under her breath.

It hadn't been her idea to come. She wasn't going to parties these days. It was all Fred's doing.

'Pop over to the flat. Pick up Plunkett's manuscript. Maybe a couple of other things. Go to Sheila's party. Do you good. There won't be any musicians there,' said Fred, who sometimes saw more than you might expect, his stepdaughter thought wryly. 'Stay the night if you like.'

Since he had turned her bedroom into an extra music room the week she moved out three years ago, the offer was less than enticing. The only bed in the place was his own four-poster with the original horsehair mattress.

'Gee, thanks,' said Alexis.

He laughed. But Fred had the trick of getting his own way, for all he seemed so absent-minded. That was really why she was here.

She had spent most of the afternoon packing up what he lightly dismissed as a couple of things which he wanted her to take out to Spain for him. That meant she hadn't managed to make her get-away before Sheila Mallory's party began. And Fred was quite capable of ringing from Tokyo to send his favourite neighbour upstairs to collect her if she didn't turn up as instructed.

Her wrist was hurting. She rotated it unobtrusively. Sheila Mallory looked up from her conversation and dived over to her.

'Alexis, my dear. So glad you've come.' She was bubbling with excitement. 'I've just pulled off the most wonderful deal. Celebration time.' She took Alexis's arm. 'Now who do you want to meet?'

Alexis looked round. As Fred had said, there wasn't a musician in sight. In fact there wasn't a face she recognised. Except . . .

She hesitated, her eyes drawn to a new arrival. He was standing in the doorway, surveying the party arrogantly. He seemed unaware of the eyes. Or indifferent to them. Maybe that accounted for the arrogance.

Just for a second their eyes met. Alexis felt a little shock, as if she knew him. He was tall, broad-shouldered and slim-hipped, with a hard, handsome face like a hawk. But it was not his good looks that made everyone look at him. It was that air of cool power. *Surely* she would remember if they had met?

But then his gaze moved on round the room indifferently and she knew they hadn't. Tension went out of her. She didn't realise she had been holding her breath.

Sheila followed her eyes.

'Fan of the Slayer?' she asked, amused.

Alexis wasn't listening. She was watching the man move through the crowd. He's *famous*, she thought, enlightened. She'd lived all her life with famous people— her mother who'd revelled in it, Fred who didn't notice— and she knew the signs. She shivered. Fame did funny things to people and the man didn't look kind.

'Who——?' she began, turning back to Sheila. Then it hit her, that melodramatic nickname. The Slayer! 'Oh, boy, am I in the wrong party,' she said involuntarily.

Alexis Brooke, struggling musician, had nothing in common with international movie stars. Especially not those with Michael Slane's reputation. All she needed to do was subject him to some of her notorious clumsiness and he'd probably break her other wrist, she thought bitterly.

Sheila laughed. 'No mayhem tonight,' she said. 'He's promised me he'll behave.' She was filled with some secret amusement. 'He's being *very* nice to me at the moment.'

Alexis was embarrassed. Her own mother had moved on from Fred to a succession of younger men, and Alexis had never known how to handle it. Michael Slane had to be a good twenty years younger than their hostess.

Her embarrassment showed. Sheila gave a shriek of laughter.

'Not like that, darling. Mickey only dates stunners. I wouldn't have qualified even in my salad days.' She paused, then, lowering her voice confidentially, went on, 'I mean I've signed him. Or I think I have, if the lawyers don't mess it up.' She crossed her fingers. 'I'm not really telling people yet, just in case. I'm superstitious. His old agent is fighting it. Using some pretty dirty tricks too.'

'Oh,' said Alexis, embarrassed again. 'I'm sorry. I didn't mean . . .'

Sheila squeezed her waist. 'Darling, I'm flattered. He's gorgeous, isn't he?' She surveyed him fondly. He was stalking across the room. It was like something out of one of his own movies, Alexis thought, awed. The crowd just parted for him. There were a couple of flashes. Someone was taking photographs.

Michael Slane's eyes narrowed. Suddenly he looked not just arrogant but tough and dangerous as well. Alexis thought with a shiver that she was glad she wasn't the photographer. Though presumably he wouldn't make a scene at a cocktail party with a hundred or so guests watching...

Even as she was thinking it, she saw him identify the culprit. He smiled. It was a flash of blindingly white teeth in the tanned face. It was completely unamused. He turned.

Alexis gasped with everyone else as he seized the camera out of the man's hands. The photographer made a grab for it but one strong brown hand dropped him where he stood. The man fell to one knee, coughing. Slane wrenched open the camera and took out a film cartridge. He slipped it into his pocket, tossing the expensive camera aside contemptuously. In the silence, you could hear the tinkle of glass as the flash attachment broke. A man stepped across his path.

'Uh-huh,' said Sheila in resignation. 'There goes his promise. Come on, Alexis. Diversion.'

Alexis protested; it was no use. Sheila took her hand and towed her through the crowd. Since Alexis was holding her glass in her right hand, Sheila grasped hold of the injured one, without realising it. Alexis winced. But Sheila, ploughing her way through the scent and diamonds like a liner through port, didn't notice.

'Mickey,' she said in a carrying voice.

Michael Slane turned slowly. The man who had accosted him stayed at his shoulder. Clearly he was waiting to regain Slane's attention as soon as the social annoyance of the two women had passed. And Michael Slane was used to people standing waiting at his shoulder.

Alexis felt a flicker of real dislike. His eyes, Alexis saw, were cold as the moon.

'You've got a British fan here,' Sheila said. 'Wants to meet you.'

The eyes flicked up and down her reluctant figure and didn't grow noticeably warmer. Sheila didn't notice that either.

'Alexis Brooke from upstairs. Her stepfather has the apartment above mine—Friedrich Schmidt, the conductor.'

Michael Slane stretched his sculpted lips in a travesty of a polite smile. It was clear, Alexis thought, between amusement and scorn, that Friedrich Schmidt was not in his Gallery of Fame. Sheila was undismayed.

'He's very famous,' she said indulgently. 'He conducts all over the world. He was supposed to be here tonight but he's performing in Tokyo unexpectedly.'

Michael Slane was faintly more interested, but not much.

'Have you been to Tokyo, Alexis?' he asked. It was a palpable effort at finding a subject of common interest. He did not even try to disguise his boredom.

The flicker resolved itself into a steady flame of anger. Alexis decided she'd go home to bed as soon as she decently could.

'No,' she said shortly.

Sheila looked at her in surprise. Presumably this wasn't the way eager fans were supposed to talk to their idol, Alexis thought. Well, just because she recognised the man didn't mean she was going to curl up at his feet and worship.

'You've been, haven't you, Mickey? Aren't they going to shoot the next Slane-Harvey movie in Japan?' Sheila said.

The man at his shoulder laughed. 'Rosie Harvey fancy herself in a kimono, Mick?'

Michael Slane shrugged. 'There was a script she liked with an Oriental heroine.'

The man was disappointed. But it was clear that he wasn't going to get any more out of Michael Slane. He wandered away, disconsolate.

Alexis thought of the tall blonde Californian actress who regularly partnered Michael Slane in his movies and her eyebrows went up. To her surprise she found Michael Slane looking at her. It seemed he shared her scepticism.

'It would have been a challenge for the make-up artist,' he agreed.

'Will it get made?' she asked, involuntarily.

The eyes iced over again. 'You'd have to ask the studio.'

Sheila said hurriedly, 'You never ask an actor about his next job, honey. They're superstitious too.'

Michael Slane raised his eyebrows. 'You're superstitious, Alexis?' he asked in that famous husky drawl.

She felt the jolt of attraction along her nerve-endings, as if she'd touched a live wire. She didn't know him; she disliked his manners; and he wasn't even trying. Alexis thought, outraged, He *can't* have this effect on me. She took a step back.

'Not me,' she said crisply. 'Sheila.' She decided to jolt him a bit too. So she gave him a sweet smile and said, 'She's not talking about you in case you disappear in a puff of green smoke.'

Sheila gave a theatrical scream of protest, muted so that it didn't bring the room to a halt. Michael Slane's eyes narrowed.

'And what does that mean?'

It was some sort of obscure challenge. Alexis realised, belatedly, that she might have done her hostess a disservice. But she wasn't backing down before Michael Slane.

'I'm sure you know better than I could. I'm not in the business. So I'm not really interested,' she said crushingly.

'Alexis——' Sheila sounded shocked.

Michael Slane wasn't shocked. Or crushed. He was faintly amused—and very, very cold.

'So what business are you in, Alexis? Are you a professional stepdaughter?'

Alexis had been thinking of herself as a parasite on Fred for weeks. But to have it thrown at her like that, as a mocking query, made her see red. She glared at him, all pretence of good manners falling away.

'Only part-time,' she said, smiling falsely.

'And the rest of the time?'

It wasn't a cocktail-party courtesy. There was a streak of steel behind the question.

'I'm a musician.'

'What sort of a musician?'

It was like an interrogation. She could sense Sheila's surprise. She lifted her chin and told him the truth.

'A severely struggling one.'

He acknowledged that with a lifted eyebrow.

'You play? Sing? Prostitute your art by writing movie scores?'

Alexis set her teeth and shook her head. 'Not me. I'm the sort of musician who starves in a garret.'

Michael Slane smiled his slow, sexy smile. It made Alexis shiver. It might be sexy but she had been right—it wasn't kind.

He nodded. 'They make movies about them,' he said drily. 'They generally end up famous.'

That hurt. Alexis managed not to wince. It was a particularly sore spot at the moment. Michael Slane wasn't to know that, of course. But it didn't make her feel any more kindly towards him. He had just called up the echoes she really must put behind her.

Things had already been bad with Patrick. He couldn't understand why she wouldn't have an affair with him when she was so plainly in love. And he wouldn't recommend her to another teacher. Alexis, remembering the kindness in his parents' house when his mother was the only person in the world who seemed to care what happened to her, couldn't bring herself to stir up gossip by asking for a change mid-term. The lessons had got more and more tense.

When she had at last, reluctantly, shown Patrick the concerto she was going to enter for the Sheldon Prize, he had flung it away from him almost as if he was angry.

'Grow up, Ally. That's not a concerto. It's a string of street songs. It wouldn't get into the last thousand of the Sheldon Prize.'

She must have looked shattered. He got angrier.

'Look, I know it must be difficult with an inheritance like yours. But you've just got to get used to the idea, Ally. You're no Mozart. You can make a reasonable living teaching. But that's it.'

And then, when she hadn't answered, hadn't known what to say, had reached to take back the manuscript . . . Her mind skipped away from the memory.

It wasn't Michael Slane's fault, of course. But he had brought that nasty little exchange back to her, and in doing so had reminded her that she had a very dubious future indeed, if she couldn't play the flute and didn't start writing music again soon. Dubious and lonely too, unless she could get over her feelings for Patrick.

'Famous?' she said, hating him. 'They're just the ones they make the movies about. Most of us starve right on to the end.'

He said softly, 'Not the ones with Friedrich Schmidt for a stepfather, surely?'

Meeting his eyes, Alexis realised with a little shock that he disliked her quite as much as she disliked him. It was quite exhilarating in its way. He obviously didn't care a snap of his fingers about anyone else at the party, one way or the other, but he had worked up quite a hostility to her on the strength of five minutes' conversation.

She said, 'Oh, I do hope not.'

She was perversely gratified by the flash of contempt in his eyes.

Sheila said in a startled voice, 'But Fred said you——'

She was going to tell him Alexis didn't show her work to her stepfather. He was too kind, too fond of her to be a fair judge. But she didn't want that piece of private information presented to Michael Slane. Alexis dropped her champagne glass.

At once everyone exclaimed, offered help, offered more champagne. Sheila summoned a waiter who returned with a small dustpan and whisked the shards away, mopping at the pale stain until nothing was visible.

Only Michael Slane didn't exclaim or offer help. As she had guessed he wouldn't, Alexis thought smugly. He met her eyes levelly over the head of their concerned companions.

'If I offer you my glass, will you throw it at me?' he drawled.

He put out a long, strong hand and twisted her efficiently away from the group, so she had her back to the wall and was talking to no one but him. Alexis was startled. This was open war. She looked round. Nobody else seemed to have heard him. And if they'd noticed his manoeuvre to get her on her own, they weren't surprised enough to do anything about it.

'Don't be ridiculous. I didn't *mean* to drop my own.'

'No?'

'No,' she said hotly. 'I'm just unlucky. Butter-fingers, we call it.'

'It happens a lot?' He seemed amused in his cold, detached way.

'Sometimes,' she admitted stiffly. 'I'm not well co-ordinated.'

'I'd say your co-ordination was ace,' he said drily. 'To say nothing of your timing. What was Sheila going to say when you lost your drink?'

Alexis glared at him. 'I have no idea. I'm a musician, not a mind-reader,' she snapped.

'Then you're a very smart lady,' he told her. 'You seem to read me pretty accurately. And we've only just met.'

Alexis jumped. Hadn't she just been thinking the same thing herself? He saw her reaction.

'Or is that because you're such a fan?' he added softly, jeeringly.

She looked him straight in the eye.

'As you well know, Mr Slane, I'm no fan of yours.'

He looked as if he'd scored a hit.

'Yeah, I thought so. They why did you want to talk to me, sweetheart?'

She remembered Sheila's fulsome introduction and flushed angrily.

'I didn't. It wasn't my idea.'

'So whose idea was it? Do a bit of freelancing for the purple Press on the side, do you, honey?'

She watched the jut of his jaw. It was not precisely aggressive. But he had the cool, resourceful look of a man who could deal with anything that was thrown at him. Which for the moment seemed to be her. Alexis was so angry, she could have screamed.

'I wouldn't have the skill to write up a career like yours, Mr Slane,' she told him with poisonous sweetness.

He gave her that slow, lazy smile that brought women back over and over again to his films.

'What's missing, honey? The vocabulary? Or the experience?'

She regretted that he hadn't, after all, given her his wine. It would have given her great pleasure to tip it over that arrogant head.

'Both,' she snapped.

'Let me help you along.' He went into a Chicago whine. 'Get it while you can—it might not be around tomorrow. That's Mickey's motto.' The mockery was harsh.

She was taken aback.

'Are you serious?'

'Why? Are you fishing for a quote?'

'Of course not.' She tried to imagine the sort of man who lived like that—and failed. 'It doesn't sound very peaceful.'

'Peaceful? Hell, who wants peace? I'm thirty-five years old and I came from nowhere. I've got a lot to catch up on,' Michael Slane said cynically. 'The papers know that. They write it.' He took her by the wrist. Fortunately it was the good one. 'And maybe you do too. Tell me about yourself, Alexis Brooke.'

She looked deep into his eyes. She had a strange sensation of falling. She dragged her wrist away and stepped back.

'Not on your life,' she said with feeling.

She didn't want to give this magnetic, unpredictable man any personal information about herself whatsoever. She didn't know what he might do with it but she didn't trust him a millimetre.

'I've never written a word of journalism in my life,' she said. 'I don't even read the papers much. I know nothing about the movies and less about you. And that's all I want to know, Mr Slane. I'll bid you goodnight.'

If she expected him to stand aside like a gentleman she was disappointed. His smile grew as he stood there, looking down at her. That smile said she was his prisoner and he knew it.

'Let me pass,' said Alexis, simmering.

Michael Slane appeared amused. 'Make me,' he invited.

She contemplated a good, high scream. That would shock him out of his taunting complacency, she reckoned. And everyone else at the party too. He'd have to explain what he was doing to make his companion resort to such extreme measures. She measured the distance between them and opened her mouth...

'Darling,' said Sheila from behind him, 'sorry. I got caught by Zach Fisher.'

Alexis closed her mouth again, feeling foolish. There was a distinct glitter in Michael Slane's eyes, she saw. He knew what she had been about to do. And he wasn't amused any more.

Well, that was some comfort at least. It was some consolation for the uneasy feeling that she had been about to make the biggest fool of herself of her life.

She smoothed her hair, grateful for the reprieve.

'I've monopolised your star guest for too long,' she said sweetly.

It was obvious that Sheila agreed with her, though she was too polite to say so. It was not obvious what Michael Slane thought. But he backed off enough to let her pass.

'Darling, go and get yourself another drink,' Sheila urged her distractedly, taking him by the arm. 'There's a bar in the corner. Now, Mickey, you've got to...'

Alexis escaped. She could hear Sheila's voice behind her, cajoling him. And she could feel his eyes following her. She walked very straight. She was *not* going to bump into anything under Michael Slane's coldly mocking gaze.

She didn't get as far as the bar. A passing waiter gave her a drink. And a passing neighbour pounced.

'Were you actually talking to Michael Slane?' she demanded, awed.

'Yes,' said Alexis shortly.

He and Sheila were lost in the crowd now.

'What's he like?' breathed the other. She was a fussy woman who regularly complained about Fred playing opera in the afternoon when she liked to nap.

Alexis sniffed. 'No horns and a tail, but otherwise just about as advertised.'

'Oh!' The woman was offended.

Someone else laughed, though. It was the photographer who had been so publicly manhandled earlier. Alexis looked at him with a good deal of sympathy.

'Born again hell-raiser, that's our Mickey,' he said ruefully.

Alexis believed it. She said, 'Did he hurt you?'

He shrugged. 'He hurt the camera more. Still, it's insured.' He laughed. 'The insurance companies are going to start adding an exclusion clause to cover Mickey Slane, if this goes on. That's the third he's totalled this week, I'm told.'

'Childish,' said Alexis. And trod on the eager neighbour's foot. The woman glared at her. She apologised. The woman turned away without a word.

Alexis sighed. Her anger was beginning to die down now. Without its warming glow, she was back to being a tall, clumsy girl in a room full of hazards.

She looked round. There were so many of them. Not only people, who moved when you weren't expecting them to, but glasses and tables and tall urns of flower arrangements on fragile antique stands. Even without the crowd it would have been an obstacle course.

Alexis bit her lip, debating.

The terrace, she thought. That was it. She was much nearer to the french windows than she was to the door. There wouldn't be anyone outside in the cool April night. She could slip up to the flat above by way of the fire escape. She began to thread her way carefully.

She did all right as far as the terrace itself. Whether it was because of her intent look of concentration or because she genuinely was improving, she managed not to step on anyone or break anything in her progress. The trouble came through the big doors when she walked hard into an unexpected body.

Alexis gave a small scream and dropped her second glass of the evening. It shattered, scattering her strappy shoes with shards. She stepped back from him involuntarily.

'Don't move,' he ordered, quick as a whiplash.

And she knew who it was.

'What are you doing out here?' she whispered fiercely.

'Following you. Hold on,' he said, sounding amused.

And before she knew what he was about he had put strong hands round her waist and lifted her high over the splinters.

'Shake your feet,' he instructed. 'You've got glass on your sandals.'

He didn't wait to see whether she obeyed him. He carried her to the far end of the terrace while she floundered in his arms, totally disconcerted. Once she felt him wince. But he kept his balance like a tightrope walker and the grip on her waist didn't falter.

He put her down. For a moment, it seemed to Alexis that his hands lingered. Her heart began to beat uncomfortably fast. She twitched herself out of his hold and said ungraciously to cover her reaction. 'Let me go, you——'

'Temper!' The husky voice with its transatlantic accent was laughing at her. Not kind laughter. 'What are you doing out here?'

Her voice rose. 'I was just going, actually. Leaving.'

He shook his head. She could just make out the movement in the dark. 'Before the dancing? You wouldn't want to miss that. I might dance with you,' he said cynically.

Alexis shivered. '*Dancing*?' The horror in her voice was unmistakable.

There was a little pause. She could feel him staring at her in the darkness.

'Correction,' he murmured. 'You *would* want to miss it. Can you be a wallflower? With your sweet nature? Surely not.'

'That's my business,' Alexis said with dignity.

The truth was that she was as clumsy on the dance-floor as everywhere else—but she would die rather than admit it to mocking, cold-hearted Michael Slane.

'I'm going home,' she said with finality.

He was still laughing. 'Over the parapet? Are you wearing a parachute under that?'

'No parachute. Just a fire escape,' she said, pointing.

He turned his head. 'So I see.' He paused fractionally and then said, so smoothly that she had no idea what was coming, 'Then I guess we have to say goodnight.'

And he took her into an embrace of what even in-experienced Alexis could recognise as pure per-formance. She pushed him away, furious. The kiss was too clinical to justify the acceleration of her pulse. She stamped her foot. She hadn't seemed to feel anything very much for so long that she had forgotten her temper. She did it too hard. The slender heel of her sandal snapped and she lurched sideways.

'Damn!' she said with real feeling.

Her antagonist looked down, his hands steadying her.

'Accident-prone indeed,' he said, amused.

Alexis snorted. 'That wasn't an accident. That was wilful damage. Started by you. Get out of my way.' She disengaged herself and turned towards the fire escape.

'Not yet,' he said, stopping her with a hand. It found her waist, just under the breast, burning through the flimsy georgette. Alexis stopped as if she had been shot.

He spun her round to face him.

'You need more than one experiment to prove a theory,' he told her. He sounded amused and hard and surprisingly determined.

His head came down. Alexis concentrated on balancing on her one good heel. Breathing became extraordinarily difficult. It wasn't the arrogant imposition she expected. Instead, he was teasing her, just touching his mouth against hers, tasting the tender skin of her inside lip. There was no pressure, no demand, no suffocating intrusion; but she still couldn't breathe properly.

This, she thought, recognising technique when she met it, was real experience. And it was way out of her league.

CHAPTER TWO

ALEXIS let herself in through the kitchen door. She dropped her shiny black sandals on the kitchen table and snapped on the light. Yes, there was no doubt. They were irreparable. She sighed ruefully and threw them in the bin.

That would teach her to lose her temper with strangers. Though after the blank indifference of the last months, she thought ruefully, it was a relief to know she could still work up a good heat.

Alexis sat down, pulling the pins out of her hair. It fell in a warm swirl about her chilly shoulders.

She had never lost her temper with Patrick. She dropped her head in her hands, flaying herself with memory. Oh, she had been *so* devoted. So unquestioning. Why hadn't it occurred to her that a man like Patrick—handsome, talented, successful—couldn't still be single?

She knew the answer, of course. He'd hidden it deliberately. He never talked about his family. After her godmother's death Alexis hadn't seen any of them for years until Patrick offered to tutor her in the long, bad summer before she went to music college eight years ago.

Even so, there was no excuse for being so naïve, she castigated herself. It wasn't a secret marriage. If she'd asked, if she'd even talked about him to somebody else, she could have found out easily enough. Hell, Fred could have told her if he'd realised.

Alexis had been overwhelmed when Patrick, returning to London loaded with honours garnered in the intervening years, insisted on teaching her, insisted on telling her he loved her. It was like a dream come true. She'd loved him, shyly and secretly, ever since that summer. And when he kissed her, she just hadn't asked herself what had happened to him in the interval.

'Damn,' said Alexis out loud. 'Damn. Damn. Damn.'

He'd been so angry when she'd flung it at him.

'Of course I'm married,' he'd said impatiently. 'I've never made a secret of it. Marianne prefers to live in Wales. She says it's better for the children——'

'*Children*?' Alexis had gasped, white-faced.

Which was when he'd lost his temper and she had found a kiss could be like a blow. Although, of course, he had not actually hit her. Then.

Her wrist was beginning to ache. She looked down at it, flexing the fingers. They hurt with relatively little movement. Still, she was lucky to have the movement she had, or so the doctors had told her. It had been a nasty accident, they said. They had been prepared for some deformity. She was very fortunate.

The trouble was, she didn't feel fortunate. She still remembered the look on Patrick's face as he hit her.

She hadn't believed it could be happening. In retrospect she wondered if she had fallen more out of shock than the actual blow. The shock was still there. She had been in love with Patrick for eight years. Now all she felt was numb.

She'd stopped seeing people. She couldn't play well enough to rehearse so she didn't even go to orchestra. For weeks she'd sat in the flat staring at blank manuscript paper.

Her sparring with Michael Slane this evening was the first time she had emerged from that fog since the accident. She gave a little laugh that broke. Now if he knew that, what a taunt Michael Slane would have to use against her.

'Move,' she told herself. 'No point in sitting here moaning. You're going to get over Patrick. And you're going to Spain tomorrow, God help you.'

Her stepfather owned a castle in the mountains in Spain. It was beautiful and remote and held mixed memories for Alexis. Normally she avoided Fred's gatherings of distinguished musicians and went to stay there on her own later in the year. But on this occasion his reliable maid had gone to visit her daughter who was having a baby, and Fred required someone he could trust to make sure the house was made ready for his guests and—more important—that the pianos were tuned. Or that was what he'd said.

So Alexis had reluctantly agreed to pick up a new symphony from his flat, along with a whole list of essential items for his house party, and take them out to Spain in his Range Rover.

Now she made coffee, asking herself why she had let him manipulate her into doing it. But the answer was easy. When she couldn't work with her broken wrist, Fred, stopping off unexpectedly between New York and Munich, had descended on her small flat and got hold of all her bills while she was pouring him a drink.

'Hey——' Alexis had said, indignant.

But Fred flapped a hand at her. 'Pay me back when you get a commission. Meanwhile don't be stupid,' he said crisply. 'Are you still going to composition lessons?'

They were with Patrick.

'No,' said Alexis quietly.

Fred glared at her. 'It's only a broken wrist, you know. It's not the end of your career. You've got to keep working. Even if you can't practise.'

'I work at home,' she said. It was a lie. She hadn't looked at manuscript paper since she'd shown her Sheldon Prize entry to Patrick. She had had so many ideas. Now they all seemed to have dried up.

Fred looked at her narrowly. But all he said was, 'Life goes on, you know.'

She'd wondered then if he'd picked up more about her state of mind than he was saying. People said he was vague, wrapped up in his work, but Alexis knew that he was capable of startling insight when he wanted. She was even half suspicious that the trip to Spain was Fred's way of shaking her up for her own good.

She sipped her coffee, counting over what she had to load into the car. The photocopying of Richard Plunkett's symphony was done, the copies posted.

'Now for the monster,' Alexis said to herself. 'That'll shake me up all right.'

The monster was her private name for the Range Rover. Fred was a man who liked gadgets, and he had had the vehicle customised to accommodate his sound systems, the peculiar instruments he occasionally carried and, if necessary, a bed for the night. None of that had added to the comfort of the springs. In addition it was a much bigger vehicle than Alexis usually drove.

She went into the sitting-room to get the keys. She didn't turn the light on. She knew exactly where they were in the small top drawer of the writing desk. She went straight to it and was bending over the desk when she caught something out of the corner of her eye.

Casually she looked round. And froze.

Out on the shadowed terrace someone was moving. She could see the figure clearly, a terror out of a nightmare, picking his way round Fred's neglected terracotta tubs. He was moving stealthily, clearly wanting to avoid detection.

She turned cold. Not taking her eyes off him, she moved sideways, stealthy in her turn. She could call the commissionaire. Maybe even Sheila. Sheila was closer and there were plenty of people down in her flat who could help to catch him. If she could remember Sheila's number. Could she remember the commissionaire's? She mustn't turn the light on to look it up or he would see . . . Her thoughts began to tumble frantically.

The prowler had been creeping along the terrace but now he suddenly turned and came towards the window. Alexis took a step backwards, barely suppressing a scream. She put a hand up to her mouth, sinking her teeth into the back of it.

He put a hand on the brass handle and twisted it hard. Suddenly there was something familiar about that muscular figure. She took her hand away and her temper went whoosh through the top of her head.

She unlocked the french window with hands that trembled.

'What the *hell*,' she said to Michael Slane in a voice that shook with anger and the release of fear, 'do you think you're doing?'

He put back his head and laughed. It was an attractive laugh, low and amused—and with more than a hint of recklessness in it.

'I followed you up the fire escape,' he said.

'Followed——?' There was no fog of indifference now. She could barely speak, she was so furious.

'The party was boring,' he said calmly, as if that explained everything. 'Move aside, darling.'

Those hard hands—she remembered their touch all too vividly—moved her gently out of his way as he came into the darkened room.

'Lights?' he said.

She clenched her fists and passed a number of things she might say to him under review. In the meantime he had found the light-switch. Fred's sitting-room was bathed in a soft apricot.

Michael Slane gave her a wicked grin.

'"Won't you come into my parlour . . .?"' he murmured. 'Or yours to be more exact.'

Alexis didn't move. 'Is this one of your stupid stunts?'

'Stunts?' he echoed innocently.

She snorted. 'Stunts. The stuff that gets in the papers.'

He shook his head. 'I thought you weren't a fan of mine, Miss Brooke.'

'You don't have to be a fan to know about the fights in nightclubs,' she said hotly.

'High spirits,' he said coolly. 'And I pay for breakages.'

She thought about the photographer at Sheila's party. 'Do you pay for damaged cameras, too?'

His mouth tightened. 'Never.'

Her voice rose. 'You deliberately smashed that camera. I saw you. Are you going to say that was youthful high spirits?'

'No,' he said evenly. 'That was a hazard of war.'

'You're completely irresponsible,' she said in disgust.

'You're probably right,' he agreed. 'Why don't you come in and shut that door? We'll both be more comfortable.'

Alexis gave an exasperated exclamation. But it was true. She was getting cold in her thin georgette blouse. She came in reluctantly, rubbing her upper arms. He watched her. She returned the look with deliberation. What she saw wasn't reassuring.

He had a strong, almost ugly face, with high cheekbones and deep scores by his mouth that made him look as if he'd lived hard and seen too much. There was a small scar along his right cheekbone. It looked old. The mouth was sensual and a little cruel. The eyes...

It was the eyes you remembered. It was there that the undeniable magnetic power lay. They were bleak and brilliant and they showed all the arrogance in the world.

The cruel mouth widened. He propped himself on the corner of Fred's precious Italian marble hall table and grinned at her.

'I've never dated a redhead,' he told her outrageously.
Alexis gasped and glared at him.

'Well, don't kid yourself you've started now,' she retorted swiftly. 'You may have talked yourself in here but any more cracks like that and you're in a fair way to talking yourself straight out again.'

He flung up a hand in a gesture of surrender.

'No, don't throw me to the wolves, Cinderella. I'll behave.'

Alexis smiled at him sweetly. 'You will,' she agreed. 'Now tell me what you're doing here. And,' she added as he opened his mouth, 'if you call me Cinderella again, I'll throw things. I haven't been to the ball and you sure as hell aren't Prince Charming. Now talk.'

Amazingly he was laughing. It was a different laugh, this time, as if he really was amused.

'I can't argue with that.' He lowered his voice conspiratorially. 'I'm on the run.'

Alexis stared at him. 'Very funny,' she said sarcastically. 'From the police or a hit squad?'

'Worse,' he said, shaking his head. 'Press,' he added succinctly.

Impatient words sprang to her lips. Her experience of the Press was confined to one or two polite foreign correspondents who were friends of Fred's and the music critics who weren't friends with anyone. But then she thought it was probably different if you were a highly newsworthy movie star.

'Why?' she said blankly.

Michael Slane shot her a sharp look. After a pause he clearly decided that her innocence was genuine. He shrugged.

'You mean in general or this particular occasion?'

'Either,' said Alexis, quite bewildered. 'Or both.'

'Well, in general, I'm front-page fodder. I'm the street kid made good who sometimes can't forget his origins.

It's real human interest stuff,' he said with savage irony. 'Particularly when I've got a new movie out.'

'And have you?'

He shook his head. 'Neither here nor Stateside. No, on this particular occasion, we're seeing—if my antennae tell me true—the battle of the agents.'

Alexis stared at him. 'Oh, you're not making any sense,' she said at last. 'For heaven's sake stop sitting on that thing. It cost thousands and Fred's convinced the cleaning lady chips it. I'll make you some coffee and you can explain properly.'

But when he told his story she felt just as confused.

'This girl—you mean you didn't know her?'

'Never even seen her in a movie,' Michael Slane said solemnly.

'And she walked in when you were in the *shower*?' Alexis said disbelievingly. 'Knowing you were there? Oh, she can't have done. It must have been a mistake.'

'She brought her photographer with her.' He sounded grim.

'But——'

'Believe me, Cinderella, I know what I'm talking about,' he interjected. 'They were setting themselves up a nice little story about how I'm still a tearaway at heart. The moment I'm away from the good influence of my loving agent, I revert to type—playing games with innocent young girls in showers. Honey, I could write the headlines.'

'Don't call me Cinderella,' Alexis flashed. 'And don't call me honey. I think you're telling me a lot of non-sense. There's no *point*.'

He shook his head. 'Oh, yes, there is. The studios make the agents. The agents make the stars. If my soon-to-be-ex-agent could persuade the studio that they were running a big risk with me when I get out of his paternal clutches . . .' He shrugged. 'Well, they could pressure me to stay with him. And if I said no—they could find they hadn't any work for me. And if the other studios heard I was bad news because I was out of control, they wouldn't be rushing in to give me work either.'

Alexis sat bolt upright. 'That's—iniquitous.'

'You've got it, Cinderella. Iniquitous it is.'

'*Don't*——'

'OK, OK. I'm sorry. You're just too easy to wind up. The red hair, I guess.'

'I am not,' said Alexis with precision, 'easy to wind up. I am particularly good with difficult children.'

His eyebrows flew up. 'Really?'

Not for the first time, Alexis wanted to hit him.

She said coldly, 'Since you say these two—journalists are still pursuing you, I conclude you beat them in the first round.'

'All I could do,' Michael Slane said with deep cynicism, 'was run. It's only in the script that right triumphs. In real life, when trouble shows up, the smart man exits left.'

'And you're smart?'

'A misspent youth has certain training benefits,' he said.

In spite of herself, Alexis laughed. 'So that's what you did? Exit left?'

His teeth showed briefly. 'Eventually. I had a score or two to pay off first.'

His reputation as a hell-raiser was obviously deserved, Alexis thought wryly.

'How?'

He gave a low laugh. 'I put the two of them under the shower and left with their camera,' he said with satisfaction.

Alexis bit back another unjustified choke of laughter. 'Both of them? How?'

'I threw a towel over them first. That way I got to shove them both in with one blow. Then I just turned the jets up and left,' he told her coolly.

Alexis struggled for the disapproval she knew she really felt. 'That was just wanton destruction,' she said primly.

He grinned. 'The camera didn't get wet. I'll even send it back. Without the film, of course.'

She shook her head slowly. Was this the cold, hard-eyed man she had clashed swords with at Sheila's party? Like this, she began to see the legendary charm.

Her safety system cut in swiftly. Look out for charm, it said. Patrick is charming. Think where that got you. Eight wasted years and a bad case of regret.

She straightened her spine and averted her gaze from the dancing brown eyes. 'And you're seriously telling me they pursued you to Sheila's party? Did they bring their towels?'

The laughter died. He was back in tough and evil mode before she had finished speaking.

He said, 'For all I know, Sheila asked them. She may not know about this evening's stunt. Or there again, she may have helped to set it up.'

Alexis was shocked and looked it before she managed to convert her expression into one of judicious doubt.

Michael said, 'Sheila's a professional and she plays rough. If I'm honest I don't expect anything else.'

'Then——'

'But so do I. And I've had my fill of bad headlines. If she wants to sign Mickey Slane the——'

'Born again hell-raiser,' Alexis murmured.

'—man no daughter is safe with—*what* did you say?'

'Born again hell-raiser,' she repeated helpfully. 'I thought it was rather a good phrase.'

His eyes sharpened. 'You're sure you don't write?'

She flicked her hair over her shoulder.

'It's not mine. That's what that photographer called you. I'm a composer—or I was learning to be. I play the flute and teach a bit to pay the bills. Writing my students' reports is the sum of my abilities with a pen.'

'A music teacher.' He leaned against the wall, thumbs in the belt of his dark jeans. He grinned suddenly. 'Now why didn't any of my music teachers look like you?'

She couldn't keep up with these lightning changes of tack. Alexis looked into his dancing eyes and found herself at a distinct disadvantage.

'Like what?' she said uneasily.

He let his glance wander up and down her while the wicked smile grew.

'Long, long red hair.' He leaned forward suddenly and took a lock of it, running it between his thumb and forefinger. 'Of course I'd have pulled it. But I'd have dreamed about it too.' The husky voice was low.

He's teasing again, Alexis thought. She stood very still and watched him play with her hair.

'And not just the hair. Big brown eyes. And a skin that smells of flowers and feels like a magnolia petal...'

He ran his finger lightly up the inside of her arm. Alexis gulped. He's teasing, she reminded herself. Don't let him get to you. Don't...

'I like your script,' she said on a croak.

He grinned and leaned towards her. He didn't take his eyes off her mouth, she saw.

'And I like the inspiration,' he said very softly against her lips.

The kiss this time was longer and gentler and much more complicated. When he drew away, Alexis felt her heart hammering so hard that it felt as if her whole body was echoing with it. She put a hand up to her throat to ease her breathing.

He drew away and smiled down at her. Very pleased with himself, thought Alexis sourly, as she strove to bring her riotous feelings under some sort of control.

'You said you'd behave,' she reminded him, out of a dry throat. She cleared it. She wished the damned cough didn't sound nervous. She didn't *feel* nervous. 'You just didn't. Out.'

The strongly marked brows flew up.

'For a little kiss?'

'That wasn't a *little* . . .' Alexis began and skidded to a halt.

'Yes, it was,' Michael Slane corrected softly. 'You know, I'm beginning to think you've got a serious hang-up, Cinderella.'

The mocking nickname was deliberate.

Alexis said calmly, 'You blew it. Out.'

Michael Slane sat down in a kitchen chair and stretched his long legs out in front of him. He looked as if he was prepared to make it a long night.

'What about a deal?' he asked.

'No deal. Out, I said.'

Alexis went to the kitchen door. He shook his head. He sank even lower in the chair, if that was possible.

'You'd throw me to the wolves of the Press corps?'

'I should think they'd all be home in bed by now,' Alexis said curtly with a glance at the kitchen clock.

He didn't follow her glance.

'They never sleep,' he assured her, watching her, as she full well knew, from under lowered lashes.

'Then you'll have to brave them some time. Why not now?'

He hesitated. 'They'll probably go by morning. They have to file their stories, you see.'

'*Morning*?' Her voice rose to an agitated squeak.

'Don't worry,' he said soothingly. 'I'll tell them we never met before.'

Alexis sat down limply. 'We *have* never met before.'

'It's always best to tell the truth.'

'But you're making it sound as if you—as if—I mean——'

'As if we're lovers,' he said helpfully. 'I know. It's a shame if that's the construction an evil world puts on an innocent truth. Don't you think?'

He met her eyes. Alexis found them warm and friendly and quite implacable. She was no more convinced by that friendliness than she was by his arguments, but she didn't see what she could do about it. She remembered the arrogance she'd seen at Sheila's party, before he'd wanted something from her. This was an actor, she reminded herself. And an actor who was used to getting what he wanted. She ground her teeth.

'You wouldn't like to know what I think,' she told him.

He laughed softly. 'You're probably right.' He stood up, stretching. 'But, one way and another, I've taken a lot of trouble to avoid the Press this evening. And you're not going to spoil it for me now.'

'Oh?' She was very polite. 'I'm not?'

'No,' he said.

She picked up the wall-mounted phone. 'Get back down that fire escape *now*. Or I'll call for help,' she hissed. 'How do you fancy a headline that says Mickey Slane spent the night in a police cell?'

'It wouldn't be the first time,' he said indifferently. 'But if you're serious...'

He stood up in a leisurely fashion. He even stretched a little. And while she was staring at him, not quite believing the ease of her victory, he twitched the telephone out of her hand and held it above her head.

It was the bad one. He wouldn't have seen her temporary splint under her cuff, of course. She bit back a cry of pain, and instead said furiously, 'You realise you could get into real trouble for this? First trespass. Now assault.'

'Assault?' He chuckled but there was a hard note in it. 'Are we back to that little kiss again?'

'No, we aren't,' she snapped, though her face flamed. She nursed her wrist. It was throbbing nastily.

From the handset he was holding above their head came the voice of the commissionaire.

'Miss Brooke? Are you there, Miss Brooke?'

'Don,' she shouted.

At once Michael Slane's hand came over her mouth like a vice. Alexis choked.

'Miss Brooke?'

He said in her ear, 'Tell him everything's all right. Or you hit the headlines with me.'

She couldn't speak, of course. But she glared up at him over his suffocating grip.

'Do you understand?'

She nodded, hating him. She could see now how he had bested the two journalists earlier. He played to win and he didn't much care how he did it.

He took his hand away slowly and gave her the phone. In a cold rage, she said, 'Get up here *now*, Don. Michael Slane is raising Cain here——'

He slammed his hand down on the telephone, cutting the connection. But it was too late, and he knew it.

'You little...'

'Yes?' She was pleased. He wasn't going to get the better of her.

'You know what you've done, don't you?'

'Called for help. I told you I would,' she flashed.

'Oh, you'll get help all right. From every gutter newshound in the world,' he said coldly. 'How could you be so stupid?'

'What are you talking about?' Alexis was impatient. 'All I've done is asked my stepfather's commissionaire to come up. That's hardly front-page stuff.'

'You told him I was here.'

'Even so . . .'

'And the lobby is crawling with newshounds.' He surveyed her, his eyes hard. 'Start thinking quickly, Miss Brooke. What are you going to say to them when you open the door?'

CHAPTER THREE

ALEXIS said slowly, 'You're exaggerating.'

Michael shrugged. For some reason that was more convincing than any protests could have been.

Her voice rose. 'I never meant——'

'No?' He was not letting her off the hook. 'Then why did you scream for help like that?'

'Because I wanted help,' Alexis said logically. She sent him a look of dislike. 'It may be your fans' idea of heaven, to be locked in an empty flat with you, but it gives me the creeps, frankly. I never meant to get involved. It's so *sordid*.'

To her surprise, she saw that she had struck home. You wouldn't have been able to see his colour rise under that impressive tan but he turned away with a small, instinctive gesture of protest.

With his back to her he said coldly, 'You should have thought of that earlier.'

'I know,' Alexis said miserably, the fight going out of her.

There was a ring on the doorbell, long and agitated. Her startled eyes flew to that uncompromising back.

'What shall I do?'

'Answer it,' he said harshly. 'It's the help you said you wanted.'

'What—what do I say?'

He shrugged.

With a catch in her voice, she said, 'Please. I've never been in a situation like this before. I don't know what to do.'

He turned then and looked at her. His eyes were angry.

'Well, you'd better put your shoes on for a start,' he said curtly. 'What do you think they'll make of what we were doing, if you open the door with your hair all over the place and your feet bare?'

Alexis flushed. But she didn't look away. If this was a small revenge of his she knew she had, at least in part, invited it. She hadn't really been afraid of him when she called for help. She knew it and so did he. She had called for help out of pure temper, sheer determination not to be beaten.

She said quietly, 'My shoes are broken. I—I've got some ballet slippers somewhere.'

'Go find them.'

The doorbell rang again, longer this time.

Alexis found her old shoes at the back of a cupboard. She pulled them on and then went to the door, running her hands through her hair to smooth it. After all, plenty of women at Sheila's party had had long loose hair. Why should anyone draw any special conclusions about what they'd been doing because hers was loose?

'It looks as if someone's just taken the pins out,' Michael said, answering her unspoken question. 'Specifically me.' He sighed. 'You really are a Cinderella, aren't you? Do you have any idea how long it takes women to make their hair look as if they've got a breeze blowing gently through it? It means a visit to the hairdresser and doing nothing else at all, hardly moving, until they go out to their party.'

'You speak from experience?' Alexis said waspishly, offended. Of course she knew; she just hadn't thought about it. She was embarrassed. She shouldn't have needed him to remind her, though.

He gave her a dry look. 'If you mean have I done it myself, no. If you mean, have I walked round a lady whose hair had been done for a party, yes, I have. Several times.'

'I pity her,' Alexis flashed.

His eyes narrowed. He gave her his charming, screen smile.

'Oh, I made up for it when we got home,' he told her outrageously.

'*Oh*!'

The bell rang again. She heard voices outside. Michael Slane had been right, then, when he'd said Don wouldn't come alone. Alexis whitened.

He looked at her without sympathy.

'If you don't answer that they're going to have the door down,' he said unemotionally.

'What shall I say?'

He shrugged. 'Whatever you want.' Then, seeing her white face, he relented a little. 'You could try the line that I left as soon as I realised it was the wrong flat.'

It sounded feeble. But there didn't seem to be much alternative. Alexis swallowed, smoothed her hair again, and went to the heavy door. Michael retreated down the hallway, silent-footed.

She had trouble with the locks. They were heavy and complicated and her wrist made her clumsy. It was not helped by Don's voice outside, asking her if she was all right.

She got the door opened eventually. There were only three of them: Don and one of the men from the front desk, and the photographer from Sheila's party.

Alexis smiled weakly. The photographer made as if to raise his camera and then, with a gesture of frustration, lowered it. Alexis was suddenly grateful with all her heart for irresponsible Michael Slane and his violence to cameras. He seemed to have put it out of action.

'Miss Brooke, are you all right?' That was Don. He'd known her when she still lived with Fred and he was genuinely anxious.

'Slane rough you up at all?' asked the photographer briskly.

Not a lot of human compassion there, thought Alexis. He didn't know or care if she was frightened or hurt as long as he got his story. Her temper began to rise again.

'No—I——'

'Break anything?'

'What?'

'Did he break anything?' said the photographer, leaning round the edge of the doorway and peering into the hall. 'He's been on the rampage once already this week. The paper's got some shots.'

Alexis glared at him. 'Thank you for your concern. No, he didn't break anything.'

'How did he get in?' That was Don. 'Did he break any locks?'

Alexis shook her head. 'Off—off the terrace. I let him in.'

The photographer looked surprised but tolerant. Alexis's skin crawled. 'I thought I knew him,' she said sharply.

'Sure.' He was still trying to see past her. 'And now you do. Where is he?'

'He's gone,' said Alexis, improvising.

Out of the corner of her eye she could see his shadow in the doorway of Fred's room.

'Scared him off,' said Don with satisfaction.

The night porter said, 'He was a guest at Mrs Mallory's. I'll check he's back there.'

'Must have been drunk,' said the photographer, amused. 'Thought he was in one of his movies, probably. Just went up the side of the building like Superman.'

'There's a fire escape,' Alexis told him coldly. 'It's perfectly safe. I use it myself.'

'Ah.' The photographer was suddenly a lot more interested in her. 'Use it this evening, did you? Did Mickey see you? Follow you, maybe?'

To her fury, Alexis felt her colour rise.

The man brought a dog-eared, spiral-bound notebook out of his inside pocket.

'How old are you, Miss Brooke? What do you do? Live here, I assume. On your own?'

Behind her there was a sharp movement in the shadows.

She said hurriedly, 'Look, thank you for coming to help but I'm very tired. Perhaps——'

'Have you met him before? Do you work in the movies?'

'I——'

'Why did you call for help? Did he make a pass? Did you struggle? Did he run off when you screamed?'

Alexis took a deep breath. 'There was a misunderstanding,' she said carefully. 'It was the wrong flat. When we sorted it out, he left.'

The photographer grinned like a fox.

'Ran,' he interpreted. 'Did——?'

But Don came to her aid. 'Well, if you're all right, we'll be going, Miss Brooke. There'a lot of people in and out of the building tonight, with Mrs Mallory's party. I don't want to be away too long.' He looked at her searchingly. 'You're sure you *are* all right?'

'I'm fine, Don. Just tired. I'm going to bed now,' she added to clinch it.

'When——?' began the photographer, oblivious.

But Don stopped him by putting a heavy hand on his shoulder.

'Then we'll go,' he said firmly. 'Goodnight, miss.'

'Goodnight.'

Alexis shut the door and leaned against it with a sigh of relief. Michael Slane came out of the doorway and looked at her without expression.

'So we're staying the night after all,' he said.

She jumped. 'What?'

He strolled forward. 'You told him you were going to bed.'

'Yes—but...'

'Good idea,' he said softly.

For no reason at all that she could think of, Alexis went bright scarlet. Michael Slane gave a low laugh.

'Yes, thank you,' he said. 'I'd be delighted to stay.'

That brought her away from the door.

'You won't,' she said firmly. 'You're going back to Sheila Mallory's.'

He shook his head. 'Oh, no. You told Peter Ravenna that I ran when you shouted. He'll get reinforcements and he'll go back to the party.' Alexis stared. 'To get my side of the story,' he explained patiently. 'And a picture, of course. Do you have any idea the blow this is going to be to my macho image?'

She said scornfully, 'And your macho image will be restored if you spend the night with me?'

He winced theatrically. 'That's unkind. I won't tell them if you won't.'

'Then——'

He put a hand on her shoulder in a patient, brotherly way that made her set her teeth. He led her gently back into the sitting-room.

'By morning Ravenna will have convinced himself he missed me,' he said kindly. 'And run out of interest in you. We can walk out separately or together and no one will know a thing about it.'

'I'll know,' said Alexis uneasily. She had a strong sense of foreboding—and she didn't want Michael Slane staying the night in Fred's flat.

He buffed her cheek lightly. 'But you won't be telling anyone.'

She looked up at him, her uneasiness growing. 'Is that a threat?'

He looked blank all of a sudden. Then his mouth twisted.

'If that's how you want to think of it.'

She said on a spurt of temper, 'Oh, this is crazy. I don't see why I should be put in this position. I'm going to call Sheila.'

Michael shrugged. 'She'll tell you that same thing. Lie low for the night and it will all blow over. Unless you fancy holding a Press call, of course.'

Alexis said with dignity, 'I shall take her advice.'

She called her. Sheila, eventually unearthed, was impatient.

'Sheila Mallory. Who is this and what's your emergency? It had better be good. I'm missing a hell of a good party.'

'Alexis Brooke,' she said. 'I'm upstairs. I have your star guest with me.'

'*What*?'

She explained. Sheila was amused.

'Well, thanks for letting me know, honey, but I'm not his keeper, you know. Or not yet, anyway. Have a nice time,' Sheila said blithely.

'Sheila——' shrieked Alexis, hearing her about to put the phone down. 'I want him out of here.'

'He'll go,' Sheila soothed. She still sounded amused. 'He's got an interview with some women's mag tomorrow morning. He'll be back in his hotel for that.'

'But . . .'

'Look, honey. He isn't breaking anything?'

'That's what the photographer asked,' Alexis said slowly.

'When he gets fighting mad he does,' Sheila said in a matter-of-fact tone. She clearly wasn't thinking of offering practical assistance. 'But if he isn't mad and he isn't drinking he's OK. Nothing to worry about. Send him off with the milkman when the paparazzi have gone. Get him,' she added as an afterthought, 'to sign Fred's visitors' book.'

She rang off chuckling.

Alexis looked at the buzzing receiver with disgust.

'Thanks a lot.'

Disgruntled, she went back to tell Michael Slane that he was right.

The sitting-room was empty.

'Michael?' she called. 'You were right. Sheila says you should leave early tomorrow.'

She went outside, puzzled. He wasn't on the terrace. Or in the corridor. Or in Fred's study. The bathroom door stood ajar and it was in darkness.

She raised her voice. 'Where are you? You'll have to stay. I'll find you a sleeping-bag . . .'

And then a nasty thought occurred to her. She went quickly to the door of the main suite and pushed it open. Inside, sprawled fully clothed in the middle of Fred's Scottish four-poster, was Michael Slane. He was deeply asleep.

Alexis surveyed him, annoyance warring with real trepidation. And then quite suddenly, now that her enemy was no longer watching her, her sense of humour revived. She began to laugh.

It was the only bed in the flat.

It was dark. She was cramped and uncomfortable. Her wrist was hurting and her feet were cold. Alexis turned fretfully and found herself gathered against a warm, muscular length. At once the chill began to disperse. She gave a little sigh of pleasure and sank back into oblivion.

She remembered it all only too clearly when she awakened.

It was her usual hour. The sun was edging the curtains with gold. But they were not her curtains.

Alexis struggled up on her elbow, pushing a hand through her tangled hair and blinking at the light. Where on earth...? Then something to her right turned and groaned and she looked down. Memory returned and horror dawned simultaneously.

She had spent the night—or a good part of it—tucked confidingly into the arm of a born again hell-raiser. Even now his arm rested negligently along the exposed length of her thigh.

Alexis looked down at that large, powerful hand. Now it was slack in sleep. She swallowed hard. Carefully she began to edge away, hardly breathing.

The hand twitched, moved, and curved possessively round her slim thigh. She froze. Her unwanted companion muttered fretfully. The hand began to move in a gentle rhythm over her skin as if he were stroking a cat. He did not open his eyes, she saw.

Alexis set her teeth and prepared to sit out the embarrassing caress until he fell back into sleep. God knew who he thought she was—if indeed he could put a name to the women he habitually woke up with, she thought cynically.

His eyes opened. Alexis stared down at him, acutely confused. For a moment the dark eyes were puzzled. Then comprehension dawned. She watched his face change, sharpen somehow and his mouth flick upwards into a smile she was coming to know. It was not a kind smile.

The questing hand slipped down to her knee, moulding it with a delicate gentleness that made her shiver. The sensation was new to her. She didn't seem able to move.

'Stop it,' Alexis said huskily.

The smile grew. He didn't take his eyes off her face. The clever fingers moved. It felt as if he was binding her in an invisible net. As if he knew he was paralysing her will.

Like some insect storing its prey, she told herself sharply. It broke the spell.

She removed her knee and prepared to slide off the bed. He stopped her by the simple expedient of reaching up and hooking a negligent hand round the back of her neck.

'Oh, *no*,' groaned Alexis as he drew her inexorably down to him.

Apart from that one swift, unforeseen movement, he had not stirred. The cruel mouth was still laughing; his eyes were still hidden. He looked almost bored; certainly indifferent. But his kiss wasn't bored. Or indifferent.

Off balance and crushed against a chest like iron, Alexis registered a kaleidoscope of sensations in a few startling seconds. I can't move, she thought. And, more alarmingly, I don't want to move.

He gave a soft laugh. 'Not what you expected?'

Alexis raised a dazed head. 'What?'

'When you came creeping into bed with me,' he explained. His voice was hard. 'After I got to sleep, I guess. At least, I don't remember asking you to sleep with me.'

'*Oh!*' Alexis struggled to free herself.

He took no notice. His eyes were like stone. His arm became a steel bar, forcing her back to meet his kiss.

Alexis fought against it but he quelled her feeble struggles. She had never felt more vulnerable in her life.

He was gentleness itself. But Alexis had the distinct impression that he was deeply angry, that the gentleness was the result of technique and manifold experience. Without that, she thought, his instinct would be to hurt her quite badly. He was punishing her for something, she was sure.

She made a suffocated protest. It died on his tongue. '*No*,' she said, muffled.

It was fruitless. He gave a little laugh under his breath and in a smooth movement turned the two of them, bodies locked, so that she was on her back staring up at muscled shoulders that blocked out the light. Her right hand was pressed weakly against his chest. Her left was trapped under her. The injured wrist began to throb. Alexis closed her eyes.

'Very good,' he said mockingly.

He kissed her eyelids. Even Patrick Montague at his most importunate had never kissed her eyelids. Alexis felt her whole body sigh with pleasure, even as she fought to resist.

She felt his fingers at the top button of the crumpled blouse. The blouse slid away and Michael bent his head to the pale flesh thus revealed. Alexis drew a sharp breath. A sensation almost like pain shot through her as his lips travelled. She moved instinctively, arching, her hands going to cradle his head.

And then real pain stabbed at her, stark and undisguisable, as her wrist twisted. She cried out instinctively. Michael froze.

'Let me up,' said Alexis, nearly frantic.

She was aware of tear-filled eyes almost as much as the burning pain in her wrist and was equally desperate about both.

Michael fell back. Alexis struggled up, holding the released arm in front of her as if it didn't belong to her. She curved over it protectively, rocking a little. Michael let her go.

'What happened?' he asked sharply.

Alexis bit her lip. The pain was dying down now but the aftermath—the terrible sense of weakness and helplessness as if she would never use the hand again—had come back with full force.

'It's my wrist,' she muttered at last. 'I broke it.'

She could feel him looking at her bent head. For a crazy moment she had the feeling he didn't believe her.

'You aren't in plaster,' he said at last, almost accusingly.

Her breathing was coming back to normal. 'No,' she said quietly. 'They took it off a couple of weeks ago. I've got a splint arrangement that's supposed to keep it rigid when it needs support. I took it off last night.'

'Why? So you could keep me warm?'

She flushed. She couldn't look at him.

'No. It gets uncomfortable after a while. I wear it mostly when I'm carrying things—shopping and so on. Or driving.'

'Or partying,' he said drily.

'Yes. Well. I don't do a lot of that.'

There was a little silence.

'Hell,' he said at last. Alexis didn't think he said it to her. He pushed the pillows up behind his shoulders and settled himself comfortably, turning to look at her. 'Is it a serious break?'

Alexis closed the fingers of her right hand round the injured wrist and flexed it cautiously. There was a slightly sickening sensation of bone moving underneath. Not for the first time since it happened she admitted the truth to herself. She didn't really know whether she'd ever be able to play again as she had in the past. And no one could tell her.

'I don't know,' she said in a low voice. 'The doctors are pleased.'

He picked that up at once. That was interesting because nobody else had. Not even her stepfather. Nor Patrick, in that brief, uncomfortable interview, although he was still notionally her teacher.

'But . . . ?' prompted Michael Slane softly.

Alexis shook her head, not looking at him. 'I don't know. I'm probably being a hypochondriac. They said it would hurt more for a while after it came out of plaster. And I don't suppose it's bad, really.'

'You sure as hell yelped as if it hurt,' he pointed out drily.

'Yes. I know,' she said in a constricted voice.

'Did I roll on it?' He sounded almost amused.

'No. It was—er——' Alexis swallowed. 'It was me. I—er—tried to move it. Only I was sort of half lying on it.'

'So *you* rolled on it.' There was no doubt about the amusement this time. He put out a hand and ruffled her disordered hair. 'Poor old Cinderella. You haven't had a lot of luck this morning, have you?'

Alexis jumped. She held on to her calm with determination.

'It could have been better,' she allowed. 'Especially if you didn't call me Cinderella. Or leap to the wrong conclusion.'

He folded his arms across his chest. The buttons of his creased shirt had come undone too, she noticed, and there was altogether too much warm brown flesh on view for her peace of mind. She averted her eyes.

'What conclusion was that?' he drawled.

'You seem to think,' Alexis told him with precision, 'that I chose last night's sleeping arrangements deliberately because it gave me some sort of buzz to share a bed with the great Michael Slane.'

'Oh. *That* conclusion.' He was unrepentant.

She glared at him. 'You're wrong, you know. If there'd been another bed here—or even a halfway comfortable sofa—you'd have been on your own. And I wouldn't have had to risk having my wrist mashed again.'

He gave a pantomime wince. 'That's a low blow,' he complained. 'You didn't tell me about your wrist.'

'I didn't tell you you'd taken over the only bed in the place either. Last night I didn't have the chance. You were dead to the world,' she informed him. 'And this morning you jumped on me before I had time to open my mouth.'

At last it registered. 'The only bed in the place? In an apartment this size? You've got to be joking.'

'Fred,' Alexis told him coldly, 'does not entertain. There are two pianos, one harpsichord, a recording-room, and a study. There's room to eat and drink and play music to your heart's content. But to sleep, guests go home. So no spare beds.'

'Good God,' he said blankly. He looked round the ornate room, and she saw him take in the cherubs on the ceiling. His mouth twitched. 'So this is the maestro's own boudoir?' There was a note of unholy amusement in his voice. 'I guess I owe you an apology.'

'You do,' she agreed.

His eyes came back to her face. There was something in the narrow-eyed inspection that made Alexis very uncomfortable.

'Consider yourself apologised to,' he drawled at last.

Alexis stiffened her spine. 'Thank you,' she said courteously. She eased her weight away from him. 'If I try to get out of bed, will you let me go this time?' she asked with a suspicion of a snap.

But Michael Slane was not at all shamefaced, as she had noticed before. He grinned.

'Sure. Especially if that's how I get to have breakfast.'

Alexis made a small popping noise like a pressure-cooker *in extremis* and bounced herself out of bed without deigning to answer. She refused to acknowledge that she heard the low laugh which followed her.

She was making coffee, muttering to herself, when the telephone rang. It was Don.

'Morning, Miss Brooke.' He sounded faintly embarrassed. 'Photographers all over the place out front.'

'Oh,' said Alexis, aware that she sounded hollow. She was embarrassed and furious about it. She tried to sound nonchalant. 'Are they actually in the garbage as well?'

'Couple of them, sitting on the dustbins,' said Don with relish, 'pointing their silly cameras at the front door. Thought you'd want to know. With all that stuff you've got to load into the Range Rover,' he added with a ponderous attempt at tact.

'Er—yes,' agreed Alexis faintly.

She sped back to the bedroom. Michael was still sitting propped against the pillows. He was leafing through one of Fred's bedside books, a luridly covered murder-mystery.

'Breakfast?' he enquired, looking up.

'No.' Alexis was too agitated to take umbrage at the high-handed assumption of service.

He frowned quickly. 'What is it?'

'Don just called. He says journalists have got the place staked out. They're lurking in the garage with their zoom lenses at the ready,' Alexis said rapidly. 'What are we going to do?'

His eyebrows went up. 'Those guys must be really desperate for a story.'

'Don't *laugh*,' she said fiercely.

Michael swung his long legs out from under the covers. They were still clothed in last night's dark trousers. He looked for his shoes.

'Under the table,' Alexis said absently. She was nursing her damaged wrist.

'I see them. Thank you.' He pulled the shoes on. 'Now what we need here is a little ingenuity.'

Alexis thought she detected a definitely patronising note. It restored her anger and with it her equilibrium. 'You're going to fling wet towels over them and make a run for it?' she asked sweetly.

Michael looked at her. 'I don't want to get a trademark. No, I think I just evaporate quietly.' He made a rapid magician's gesture in the air. His hands were long-fingered and eloquent. 'Gone where only the Shadow knows,' he said in thrilling tones.

'Down the waste disposal?' Alexis said acidly. She was a little shaken by her own reaction to those graceful hands. He hadn't even been looking at her and she reacted as if he'd touched.

'No.'

He was rebuttoning his shirt. Remembering all too vividly how it had come undone—and who had undone it—Alexis went hurriedly to the window and made a great show of looking out.

'See anything?' he asked, fastening his cuffs with little silver links.

He came up behind her.

'N-no.' He was too close. She moved away. 'But then I'd only see them from here if they were out in the driveway.'

His glance down at her was enigmatic. 'Yes, you would, wouldn't you?'

For some reason she felt her colour rise.

'What are you going to do?' she said hastily.

He smiled. But his eyes were hard. 'You're going to smuggle me out. In disguise.'

'I——?' She broke off. 'You're out of your mind. How could I? I haven't got any of my clothes here and even if I had you're too tall.' She looked at his unshaven jaw and broad shoulders. 'And you don't look like a woman.'

'I don't want your clothes,' he said, smooth as milk. 'I want you.'

'*Me?*' It wasn't much more than a squeak.

His eyes danced suddenly. 'Well, your escort.'

'What do you mean?' she demanded suspiciously.

He perched on an eighteenth-century rosewood escritoire. It wobbled. Alexis was beyond protesting.

'Well, you're leaving this morning anyway. Everyone knows you're leaving. The porters. Your neighbours. Maybe even the guys with the lenses.' He shrugged. 'So you take me with you.'

Alexis recovered her cool.

'You think they won't notice? I mean, you're not exactly inconspicuous. And they know who they're looking for.'

'Disguise,' he repeated tranquilly. 'Your friend the porter will have a spare set of overalls. Nobody looks at a guy in overalls, especially when he's carrying a pretty woman's cases,' he added drily.

Alexis was too preoccupied to rise to that one, though she sensed a blatant challenge.

'Why should he?'

'Because he's a romantic at heart like everyone else and you're going to tell him all about how it was love at first sight, and how we need time together alone,' Michael said promptly.

'I will not,' Alexis returned equally promptly.

'Yes, you will. It's your fault anyone knew I was here at all. You,' he said meeting her eyes firmly, 'owe me.'

As he predicted, Don was touched by the story. Alexis listened in silent fury while Michael explained. He didn't actually say anything she could object to, but his whole manner hinted at an explosion of passion that made her face burn. Don lent him a smart chauffeur's uniform and his blessing.

'How can you?' Alexis whispered fiercely, as they went back to the flat up the stone service stairs.

'What did I say?' Michael asked innocently.

'It isn't what you *said*,' she said coldly. 'It was the way you made it *sound*.'

He laughed. 'I'm an actor.' He sent her an enigmatic look. 'Don't get excited, Cinderella. You're nearly rid of me.'

'I hope you're right,' said Alexis sourly.

Back in the flat, she re-affixed the brace round her wrist, snapping the self-adhesive tapes with concentration. Michael looked at it curiously.

'You can really drive wearing that thing?'

Alexis gave a small laugh. 'A damn sight better than I can without it. Now that *really* hurts.'

He frowned. Alexis was checking Fred's list one more time and didn't notice.

'Would you call the lift, please?' she asked. 'We put all the luggage into it and drop straight down to the car park.' She picked up one of the bags.

He took it from her. 'You call the elevator. I'll do the scene-shifting.'

He was as good as his word. She didn't carry so much as the container of compact discs. In the muted light of the underground car park, Alexis unlocked the Range Rover and Michael loaded it. He was fast and efficient. The photographers at the entrance didn't even look round.

He took the keys from her.

'Get in.'

She stared at him. 'But——'

'I said, get in,' said Michael, swinging himself up behind the wheel.

Alexis stood her ground. 'That's my stepfather's car. Get out of there. You can't drive it.'

He flicked up an eyebrow. 'Honey, if it's got wheels, I can drive it,' he assured her.

'No. I meant——' On the point of stamping her foot, Alexis restrained herself. 'I mean that is not your car.

And I haven't given you permission to drive it,' she
added, her voice rising.

One of the photographers looked round.

Michael leaned across and opened the passenger door.

'Get in,' he said again, unimpressed.

She didn't. Instead she leaned into the car and hissed
at him, 'You get out from behind that wheel, Michael
Slane, or I'll have you on the front page of the newspapers as a car thief.'

He wasn't looking at her. He was looking straight
ahead. Which was why she was unprepared when a muscular arm shot out and snaked over her left shoulder.
As he hauled her on board she heard the back of her
blouse tear.

So did the photographers. Both swung round. Almost
at once they were running towards the car, cameras up.

'So you will,' he said coolly. The vehicle was already
moving. 'If you don't want to fall out, close that door,'
he advised.

Alexis did so. It jogged her arm badly. In spite of her
anger, she cried out at the sick pain that shot up her
arm. He sent her an unreadable look.

'Either lean forward and hide behind your hair or
smile,' he advised her. 'You're about to have your picture
in the paper.'

And they shot out of the garage with flashes like
gunfire blinding her.

CHAPTER FOUR

ALEXIS sat hunched beside him, her arm clutched against herself, hating him. He sent her a cool look.

'Cheer up. Even if the picture isn't good, they'll get your name from the guy on the desk. Your friends will find out.'

She turned her head to glare at him. His vanity was intolerable. Did he think she *wanted* people to know she'd been seen driving off with him from Fred's flat early on a Sunday morning? What on earth would they think had happened on Saturday night?

'Find out I've been kidnapped?' she queried between her teeth.

He shrugged. 'If that's the way you want to tell it.'

'What other way is there?' she snapped.

He swung the heavy vehicle round a tight corner, not answering. He glanced in the driving-mirror.

'Nobody following. Yet, anyway.'

Alexis clenched her fists. 'Answer me, you—you—hooligan. What is this if it isn't a kidnap?'

He flicked a glance her way.

'Well, now, it could be a number of things,' he drawled. 'Like a set-up.'

'*What*?'

'A rather cleverer publicity trap than the first,' he explained pleasantly.

Alexis shook her head, bemused. 'Are you trying to say *I* set you up?'

'Didn't you?' His voice was hard now. 'It was you who called the porter last night, after all. And it was you shrieking like a kid in a horror movie back there.'

Alexis gasped with the injustice of it. 'You were stealing my stepfather's car.'

He made an impatient noise. 'Are you seriously saying you could drive this thing?'

'I've never had any trouble in the past,' Alexis said with dignity and a less than strict regard for the truth.

He pulled the Range Rover into the side of the road so abruptly that she had to put a hand on the dashboard to steady herself.

'OK. Turn the wheel and hold on to it,' he said crisply.

'What?' She was confused. 'Don't be silly. I'm not in the right seat. It's an awkward angle...'

'Not that awkward. You want to drive this damned car—you show me you can hold it on the road. Do it.'

She did, muttering. It cost her a good deal of pain. And in the end she couldn't hold the wheel in place. She sat back, biting her lip.

'Hurt yourself?' Michael didn't sound sympathetic.

She set her teeth. 'Yes. What was the point?'

'To demonstrate that you *can't* hold it,' he told her without emotion. 'It's too heavy and you're still in pain. If I hadn't driven, we wouldn't have got out of the garage without taking a couple of other cars with us.'

Alexis pushed back the tangled red hair.

'Nonsense,' she said coldly. 'I'm taking the Range Rover to Spain this afternoon. My stepfather wouldn't have asked me if he didn't trust my driving.'

There was a sharp silence. Then, '*Spain*?' Michael said unbelievingly.

'Why not?' she demanded. 'Women are licensed to drive there, you know.'

'If they're all as stupid as you, then they shouldn't be,' he said. He was white round the mouth. 'You couldn't drive a grocery trolley at the moment.'

Alexis shouted, 'Stop patronising me.'

He said very slowly and clearly, 'You are clearly injured. What sort of stepfather tells you to take this four-wheel drive lumber-room to Spain? I gather you were thinking of going alone?'

Alexis was so angry, she could have hit him.

Instead she said sweetly, 'Unless you'd like to come along too, yes. And he's the best sort of stepfather. After my mother married him he——'

'That's not a bad idea,' Michael said slowly.

'—couldn't have looked after me better if he'd been my real father.' Alexis stopped dead. '*What* did you say?'

'I said it's not a bad idea.'

'You're crazy,' Alexis said wearily. She had been saying it without noticeable effect for over an hour. She had said it all the way back to her Hampstead flat, between having directions extracted from her. She had said it while he prowled round her home, making it look suddenly smaller. He was no longer even pretending to listen.

She lived in a converted Edwardian house she'd bought the year she went to college. Fred had given her the money. He'd told her she needed to make her mistakes in decent privacy. But she hadn't, thought Alexis, made any mistakes at all, except the big one of falling in love. Until now.

Watching her uninvited guest, she wondered what sort of mistake he was going to turn out to be. Well, at least she wasn't going to fall in love with him, she thought. After Patrick she was immune.

The ground-floor flat gave on to a fair garden. Michael strolled over to the window and looked out. The garden was full of grape hyacinths and late daffodils. A marmalade cat was picking its way through a tangle of rosebushes.

'Dustbin Dan,' said Alexis. 'Poor creature, he must be starving,' she added resentfully. 'My neighbours are feeding him for tonight. But I hadn't bargained on staying out yesterday. He's two meals behind.'

The cat pushed its head and forepaws through the cat-door and yowled in reproach. Michael winced.

'So I hear.' He looked at the cat with disfavour. 'Does it always sound like that?'

'Only when he's hungry,' Alexis said, busy with a tin of cat-food. 'Normally we have very regular habits.'

She put Dan's saucer down in its usual place and gave him fresh water. Michael Slane watched her ironically.

'That sounds pretty committed. Just the two of you here, is it?'

Alexis knew he was pointing out that there wasn't any evidence of a man's presence in the tiny flat. She flushed. Did he think everyone had live-in lovers?

She said stiffly, 'I'm sure you know the answer to that.'

He flicked up an eyebrow. 'Find cats easier to live with than people?'

She said carefully, 'It wasn't really my choice. Dan adopted me. He was only a bedraggled kitten then. He hung around for a couple of weeks. Every time I came home from shopping, he darted in with me before I could shut the door. So in the end I gave up.'

She stroked the cat's head. He didn't stop eating, purring already. Michael watched. She straightened.

'And if you mean do I think cats are more reliable than men,' she added militantly, 'the answer's yes. In my experience.'

The brown eyes were shrewd. And mocking.

'You want *reliable*? Sounds like a dull life,' he murmured. 'Do we take him with us?'

Alexis sighed. '*We* don't do anything. You go back to your hotel. I go to Spain. Dan stays here and gets looked after by neighbours.'

He ignored the first part. 'Doesn't he fret?'

'When I go away, you mean? No.' She tickled the cat briefly behind the ears. 'He doesn't fret. He knows I always come back to him.'

'Must be a good feeling.'

Alexis detected mockery and glared. She stood up, rubbing her hands down the sides of her skirt.

'Yes. Well. I must go and change and throw my tooth-brush into my case...'

'Got a spare?'

She turned to face him. 'Look, Michael, you're crazy. I know you don't want to listen but you can't possibly come with me. You need a passport and money and——' She broke off. 'Don't you see, it takes *planning*?'

'You mean if we'd planned it in advance, you'd have no objection to my company?' he asked softly.

She sent him a look of undisguised dislike. 'That's not what I meant and you know it.' She hesitated. Then, 'What would people say?' she burst out in exasperation.

'Well, I wasn't figuring on telling anyone,' Michael drawled in his laziest accents.

Alexis sent him a look of disgust. 'Don't be rid-iculous. You'd have to tell someone. What about your job? Your friends?'

'Honey,' said Michael cynically, 'a man like me doesn't have friends. Employees. Employers. Parasites. And that's it.'

'Sounds as if you could do with a cat too,' she told him, not without satisfaction.

To her surprise, he flung up a hand in acknowl-edgement of the shot. She also saw, to her even greater surprise, that he was laughing. When he laughed,

Michael Slane had the compulsive attraction the legends ascribed to the old gods, Alexis thought with a shiver of trepidation. You might be suspicious as hell, you might not want to surrender—but you felt yourself warmed and charmed and brought dangerously close to accepting intimacy. Even wanting it... It was just as well she was immune.

He said drily, 'There's certainly never been anyone who was sure I'd come home to them.'

Alexis could believe it. She said gruffly, 'What about your job, then?'

He flung himself down on the rickety sofa and grinned up at her.

'The job's done. I've been raising Cain ever since,' he said frankly. 'All of a sudden the media have noticed. Thanks to you. God knows, I was bored enough anyway. I don't want to spend the rest of the week dodging the Press. Especially not when they start digging. You owe me, Alexis Brooke.'

'I do nothing of the kind,' Alexis said hotly. 'It was entirely your own fault...'

'Over-reaction,' he said calmly. 'I've never met such a jumpy girl in my life.'

'And I've never met such a vain, complacent, dictatorial, irresponsible——'

'OK,' he said. 'OK. I get the picture.'

He was laughing, she saw. It did not assist her temper.

'You mess up my evening, my commitments, and you expect me to do just what you want because you say so,' she accused.

His eyebrows rose. 'What commitments?'

Alexis was thrown off her stride.

'What? Oh—I should have been back here last night.'

His expression was wry. 'To feed the cat. I know.' He looked down at Dan, who was rubbing his head round shining black leather boots. Hand-made, no doubt, thought Alexis sourly. 'Sorry, buddy.'

She could have stamped her foot.

'And that's made me behindhand today. I should be off by now,' she said. She wished she didn't sound sulky.

'To Spain?' Alexis nodded impatiently. 'If you're behind schedule, you need a co-driver to make up time,' Michael said blandly.

'Once and for all,' said Alexis between her teeth, '*no*.'

Michael shook his head sadly. 'You're not being reasonable.'

'*I'm* not...'

'Look at this logically,' he invited, crossing one long leg over the other and smiling up at her as if they were friends. 'You go off to Spain, leaving me here. I call a cab. I tell them how I got here—who you are—probably who your stepfather is.' He paused. 'Cab drivers have great Press contacts,' he told her softly.

Alexis sat down. 'You wouldn't,' she said. She didn't say it with much conviction.

'It would worry you? If it got out that we spent the night together?' he asked curiously. 'You're not a child. And you don't appear to be committed. Why?'

Alexis thought of Fred's disappointment. He'd never said anything but she knew he'd been desperately hurt by her mother's promiscuity. It would hurt him all over again to think that Alexis was on the same road. And Patrick—— She blenched, swallowing. Patrick would be so angry, she couldn't begin to think what he might do.

Instinctively she hugged her wrist against her.

'It would worry me,' she said curtly. 'Especially as it isn't true.'

An odd little smile played about his mouth. 'Then you've got yourself a chauffeur, honey. Like it or not.'

Alexis looked into the smiling face and saw implacability. She gave up.

To her annoyance, Michael was right when he said he didn't need to contact anyone. He had a case full of credit cards and a battered passport in his hip pocket.

'At least tell the hotel,' Alexis besought him. 'Or you'll be reported as a missing person and we'll have the police after us.'

He laughed at her.

'What a cautious little thing you are. OK. One warning notice. My new agent can sort things out for me.'

He made a crisp phone call to Sheila which Alexis took steps not to overhear. She changed swiftly, cuddled Dan, and took her small suitcase to the bedroom door.

Michael strolled over and took it out of her hand. 'Sheila wasn't awake enough to ask questions,' he said with satisfaction. 'Now, how's your map-reading?'

His mood did not, of course, stay so sunny. He hated the ferry and hid behind darkened glasses and his leather bomber jacket in case he was recognised. He didn't like the speed of the traffic on the motorways either, especially the juggernauts. He didn't like the rain. But on the whole, apart from a couple of disputes about Alexis's map-reading, they got on pretty well.

He drove well, she learned—fast but safe. He never lost an opportunity but he didn't take risks. And, when the rain was blinding and the traffic slowed to a crawl, he neither lost his temper with the car, nor with her. As he turned the nose of the Range Rover gently off the main highway to begin the final climb to Las Aguilas, Alexis was moved to compliment him.

'You're a very good driver, aren't you?' she said, watching the strong lean hands on the wheel.

Michael slanted an amused look down at her. 'I've been driving since I was nine.'

Alexis was shocked. '*Nine*? I don't believe you. That has to be against the law.'

His eyes glinted. 'You always stay inside the law?'

'Of course,' said Alexis, and wished at once that she hadn't. To cover up she said hastily, 'Where on earth were you living? Why did people let you get away with it?'

'I lived on the wrong side of the tracks in half the States in the Union,' Michael told her evenly. 'There were other things to worry about. The lawmen were too busy trying to keep the pushers off the kids and the kids off the streets.'

'Oh,' said Alexis in a small voice.

She was shaken. She looked at him sideways—the hawk's profile and that air of being able to handle anything he had to. Yes, she could imagine him in the tough background he described.

She said, 'How did you——?' and broke off. It wasn't exactly tactful to ask him how he'd broken out of it.

But he laughed as if he knew what she was going to say.

'How did I get off the streets and into the big time?' There was an edge to his voice, something hard and reckless in the handsome face as he looked at the road ahead. 'Anger, mostly. And sheer cussedness. I knew I had talent. I didn't see why a lot of cheque-books and establishment men should keep me out in the cold.'

Alexis digested that. For the first time she felt some stirrings of fellow feeling. Patrick was certainly doing his best to keep her compositions unheard. She had always been certain of her talent, too. Until...

She said curiously, 'No doubts?'

His mouth slanted. 'I couldn't afford doubts. The studios had enough of those. Even my agent.' His mouth snapped shut. The handsome face was suddenly bleak.

'What about you?' he said, patently closing the subject. 'You must have agents falling over themselves.'

Alexis was startled. 'What? Why——? Oh, you mean because my stepfather's famous.' She shook her head ruefully. 'It doesn't work like that in classical music, I'm afraid.'

'Sure it does,' Michael drawled. 'You just haven't learned the buttons to press.'

Her brief fellow feeling dwindled sharply.

'Not in my family,' she said coldly.

He shook his head. 'You sound as if you live in a fairy-story. What is this crazy family, for God's sake?'

Alexis looked out at the rain. The road they were on was relatively quiet. She had stopped jumping every time a lorry surged past them, though she still felt vulnerable, sitting in the seat where the driver would sit in a local car. Was her family so odd? She had never thought about it before.

She said, 'There's only Fred and me now. He married my mother when I was twelve. She died five years later.'

Five stormy, frantic years of fights and flights; of sudden departures and equally unexpected arrivals. A teenage Alexis had hardly dared to answer the door, for a while, because of the disappointment when it was not her mother returning.

'Were you close?' he asked.

Alexis looked at him suspiciously but he was only making conversation. His expression was indifferent, his eyes on the road.

'No,' she said. She gave a sigh, then laughed a little, surprised by the extent of her confession. 'Do you know, I've never said that before? Maybe not even admitted it to myself. No, my mother wasn't close to anyone. She was close to her public, her audience. She loved them and they adored her. But individuals——' She shook her head. 'It was as if she couldn't quite bring us into focus.

She loved us. But a lot of the time she couldn't *see* us——' She broke off, self-conscious. 'Am I making sense?'

'Perfectly,' Michael said in a dry tone. 'Don't forget I have a devoted audience too. What happened to your father?'

'Divorce.' Alexis was abrupt. 'Not very friendly divorce. My mother was world class and he wasn't. He sends me presents at birthday and Christmas.'

'So your stepfather is your security blanket,' he mused.

Alexis flushed. 'Nonsense. I've lived on my own for ages.'

He sent her a quick look.

'On your own. Yes. That intrigues me. A girl like you should be able to do better than that,' he said reflectively.

Alexis was furious. She pressed her lips together. She was pretty sure he was deliberately winding her up. She was not going to give him the satisfaction of reacting.

Michael gave a soft laugh. 'No comment?'

She said sweetly, 'Would you like to tell me about *your* private life?'

He laughed again. 'What's private? If you've read the magazines you know the names.'

'I have not,' said Alexis, stiff with outrage, 'read the magazines.'

'Now that I can believe,' he murmured. 'What do you want to know?'

'What?' Alexis stared at him. 'I don't want to know anything about the sordid details of your affairs.'

'You asked,' he pointed out, putting the Range Rover competently into a mountainous double bend. 'You must want to know something.'

Alexis averted her eyes from the drop and said hurriedly, 'Oh, what's the name at the moment, then?'

Michael gave a little nod as if he was satisfied.

'I thought that would be it. There isn't a lady at the moment. There hasn't been for longer than you'd believe. Oh, the columns say there's a thing between Rosie Harvey and me, but that's just the Press agents.'

There was something in his voice that distracted Alexis from the terrors of the terrain.

'Do you—like her?'

'You mean, do I wish it were more than Press agents' rubbish?' Michael's face was unreadable. He shrugged. 'No chance of that. Like your mum, Rosie's not too good at focusing on anything beyond her career. Up to now I've been good for it.'

Alexis was intrigued. 'Up to now? You mean you're changing? No more Slane-Harvey movies?'

His face was absolutely closed. 'Who knows?'

Alexis felt as if she'd been slapped. She withdrew back into her seat, biting her lip.

A car came towards them in the middle of the narrow road. Michael executed a neat avoiding manoeuvre and took them smoothly into the next double curve without touching the brakes. She looked at the lean, powerful hands on the wheel and let out a long breath.

'You really are good!' she exclaimed involuntarily.

He smiled. Or at least, she thought, his mouth did. His eyes stayed black and unreadable.

'Well, you know what they say.' Alexis looked enquiring. 'A good driver is a good lover,' he told her, amused. 'What do you think?'

'Oh!' said Alexis in a furious voice. 'I don't... I mean, I wouldn't know.'

He cocked an eyebrow at her. 'Now is that because you don't know any good lovers or any good drivers? Apart from me, of course.'

Alexis considered a number of possible ripostes. Every one of them would offer him the opportunity of further innuendo at her expense. Reluctantly, she abandoned them all and took refuge in lofty silence.

She maintained it—to his evident amusement—until she had to direct him to turn off the metalled road.

'Communication restored,' he murmured. 'I thought we'd be using smoke signals soon.'

Alexis said resentfully, 'I've known you two days——'

'And two nights,' he interrupted in a soulful voice.

She ignored that and went on firmly, 'You don't know me at all and yet you insist on making remarks like that. Why do you deliberately try to embarrass me?'

For a moment he didn't answer. Then he said thoughtfully, 'Don't you think your embarrassment threshold is kind of low?'

Her resentment increased.

After a pause he went on, 'How old are you, Alexis?'

'Twenty-five,' she said in a clipped voice.

'Twenty-five? So why do you behave as if you're ninety?' he asked amiably. 'A sheltered ninety.'

'I don't.' She sounded sulky and she knew it. She couldn't do anything about it. It infuriated her.

He shrugged, looking straight ahead at the stony track which wound up the slope. The movement was eloquent of dissent. So was the expression on his face. Yet again, Alexis had the unusual urge to hit him. She clenched her hands in her lap.

'You know, I've never felt about anyone the way I feel about you,' she told him conversationally.

He looked surprised. One eyebrow flicked up and the wicked, slanting smile dawned.

'Why thank you, ma'am,' he drawled.

'I didn't mean that.' It was almost a scream.

He laughed. 'No one would think you did,' he said mockingly. 'You're just too easy to tease. It comes from those old-fashioned ways of yours.'

'I am not,' said Alexis between her teeth, 'old-fashioned.'

'Oh, yes, you are.'

He negotiated the Range Rover round two right angles, with brambles plucking at the paintwork. If she had been driving, Alexis would have stopped and edged forward. Michael took it slowly but he didn't hesitate. And, although he was concentrating sufficiently to complete the manoeuvre without mishap, it did not have his whole attention.

'In two days, Cinderella, all I've learned about you is the things you don't do. It makes it kind of hard to know how to get to know you.'

Alexis was spared the trouble of answering as he finally turned the car out of the brambles and olive trees on to the last stretch of the road. It was a small gorge, the path winding up between rocks. The vegetation was down to scrub here. But the grandeur of the soaring peaks more than made up for it.

Soaring peaks and, of course, the turrets of Las Aguilas. Alexis looked at her stepfather's castle as if for the first time. And was astonished.

Michael, whom brambles, potholes and rocks had not disturbed a whit, braked hard.

'What—is—*that*?' he said.

Alexis cleared her throat. 'Las Aguilas. Fred bought it years ago before he married my mother. It's medieval. At least originally.'

'This I can see.' He shook his head. 'If I hadn't seen it with my own eyes, I wouldn't have believed it. Does he have cauldrons of boiling oil and resident witches to go with it?'

'It's a historical monument,' Alexis said stiffly. 'There are quite stringent requirements by the Ministry of Culture...'

'Boiling oil?'

'Of course not,' she snapped. 'It's not a big castle——' he choked on a laugh but she refused to acknowledge it '—and it's way off the beaten track. It was virtually ruined before Fred bought it. So a lot of what looks authentic is actually restoration. But scholars still come sometimes.'

'Scholars. Magicians. Weirdos. They'd all fit in.' He laughed again. 'He must be loaded, this stepfather of yours. And I guess it's all normal to you, huh? You're used to his sort of thing.'

Alexis looked at him, surprised by an odd, harsh note under the laughter. He didn't wait for an answer. He drove through the open gates into the stone courtyard. In contrast to the forbidding terrain through which they had made their way, it was a riot of colour. There were tubs of geraniums everywhere and a huge vine grew up an ancient wall.

Michael shut off the engine and looked round.

'I don't believe it,' he said at last. 'I just—don't—believe it.'

Alexis got out of the Range Rover stiffly and stretched her arms above her head. She drew in a grateful breath of the cool, still air. It had been raining here too. But now the sun was out and there was a glittering freshness about everything.

'It's so beautiful here,' she said softly, remembering.

Michael came to join her, an odd look on his face. 'Home?'

Alexis shook her head. 'Oh, no. When my mother was alive we hardly ever came here. She thought it was too far away from everywhere. And too strange. Like you. But I spent a summer here once.'

She remembered the summer all too clearly. Oh, Patrick, Patrick. He hadn't been married then, of course. He'd been young, with his way to make in the world. They'd wandered through the olives and mountain meadows hand in hand. But they had never been lovers. She'd spent the next eight years of her life waiting for him to love her. And when he did... Alexis put the memories away from her, wincing.

'It's the marvellous wild country. I'll show you, if you like,' she said with constraint. 'Before you go.'

'Thank you,' Michael said. He studied her. 'Alone?'

She was lost.

'The summer you spent here,' he explained. 'Were you alone?'

Damn him, thought Alexis. Damn him for his nasty mind and his even nastier way of looking through her to her innermost secrets. How did he do it?

'There was a music tutor,' she said coldly.

'Only one? You must have been pretty lonely, just the two of you up here all summer,' Michael said idly.

Alexis swallowed. 'Oh, it's not as isolated as it looks. There's a path down to the village. You can get there in twenty minutes. And anyway, we were working.'

His eyebrows rose. 'How old were you?'

She fought a blush. 'Seventeen,' she said as if it were an admission of guilt.

'And you *worked* all summer?' he queried mockingly. 'How old was he?'

'Twenty-eight,' she said and then caught herself. 'How did you know it was a man?'

He grinned lazily. Not, she thought, very kindly. 'I didn't. But I wanted to know.'

Alexis was furious, mostly with herself. She sought for something caustic to say and failed.

He caught her eye and his mouth slanted. He patted her arm. 'Don't fight it,' he urged. 'Slap my face.'

There was a frosty silence, while Alexis strove with her dignity. Dignity won, but only just.

'I wouldn't dream of it,' she said, stepping away from him. 'You must be tired after all that driving. The least I can do is give you a meal.'

She stalked into the castle, trying hard not to hear the soft laugh with which he followed her.

The kitchen was still basically medieval, high-roofed and stone-flagged. There was a huge range across one end of it and, at the other, an impressive studded door. Michael went through. He came back amused.

'It looks like the mad scientist's lab in there. What *is* it?'

Alexis, who was inspecting the contents of a deep cupboard, looked up.

'The generator-room and back up. The freezers. The refrigerator. Emergency equipment. Batteries.'

Michael nodded. 'And the oxygen tanks?'

Alexis was startled. Nobody ever noticed those when they went into what Fred called his engine-room.

She said with some respect, 'It's the mountain rescue stuff. We're part of the network. Climbers sometimes get into difficulties on the mountain. There's a voluntary team in the village but we keep some of their equipment here—partly because we're further up, so they don't have to carry it so far, partly because it's convenient to bring back the injured here. Fred's got radio equipment if the telephone is out. And helicopters can land here.'

'A real outpost,' he said, impressed. 'Do you bring food up by mule? Or do the Air Force make drops?'

Alexis was rummaging in the store cupboard. 'We grow quite a lot. There's a kitchen garden. The rest gets brought up from the village in a truck.' She lifted her head. 'But we seem to have missed the delivery,' she said ruefully.

'Cupboard bare?'

'No. But there's no fresh food.'

'Try the fridge,' he suggested.

'Oh, Consuelo wouldn't be using that at this time of year, not when there was plenty of room in the cupboard. Feel it. It's icy.'

Michael strolled over to her and put his hand into the cupboard. 'Yeah. But let's just check the fridge, huh?'

He was right. Alexis suppressed her annoyance. Michael raided the cellar and came back with a tar-black bottle of wine.

'I think that may be very grand,' Alexis said doubtfully.

'You deserve it,' he told her, working on the cork with casual expertise. 'And so do I, by God. It doesn't say "Don't touch". So pass your glass.'

They were sitting at the big oak table in the middle of the kitchen. They ate the food she'd prepared hungrily and then sat over their glasses with a plate of fruit and cheese in the middle of the table. Michael cut a sliver of cheese from time to time but Alexis was too sleepy to eat more. She did not protest, though, when Michael opened a second bottle.

The wine was smooth and warming, with a faint flavour that reminded Alexis of something else. 'Something like sitting in front of a fire with the light dying. Watching the flames and listening to them popping. The smell of oranges,' she said dreamily.

Michael looked impressed. 'You get all that out of a drink?' He shook his head. 'That must be what Mo meant when he said I had no palate. I don't get anything out of this glass but the taste of fruit and the effect of alcohol.'

Alexis was intrigued. 'Don't you drink wine?'

Michael was affronted. 'I'm a Californian. At least by adoption. Of course I drink wine. I just came to it too late to pick up the jargon.'

Alexis put her elbows on the table and leant her chin on her clasped hands. She surveyed him a little owlishly.

'No wine on the wrong side of the tracks? I can imagine.'

'I doubt it,' he said.

She had an odd feeling for a moment that he was going to lean forward and touch her. Instead he leaned back in his chair abruptly and thrust his hands in his pockets. His face was unreadable suddenly.

But when he spoke he sounded faintly amused. 'Haven't you had enough? I don't know how good this stuff is but it certainly packs a punch. Why don't you go and lie down while I unload the Range Rover?'

'My responsibility,' Alexis said, not without a certain amount of difficulty. It rather surprised her. She gathered herself together and enunicated carefully, 'Why should I lie down? I'm not tired.'

'Not yet, maybe.'

Her eyes narrowed. 'Are you saying I'm——?' She groped for a word. 'Sloshed?' she produced.

'No, no.'

'Because I'm not. Drink,' she said magnificently, 'has no effect on me.'

She noticed her wine glass was empty and pushed it rather impatiently across the table to him. He raised an eyebrow. Alexis drummed the glass up and down on the table-top. He shrugged and poured the dark red liquid into it.

Michael leaned back, his thumbs in the belt of his jeans, and gave her a long, slow smile. Alexis had the uncomfortable feeling that something about it was dangerous. His eyes were curiously intent.

'Are you sure?'

'Of course I'm sure.' She was irritated. 'I've been drinking wine all my life. It has no effect at all.'

'The inhibitions go a lot sooner than the ability to walk in a straight line, you know,' Michael told her huskily.

'I don't have inhibitions,' Alexis retorted.

'Then how come I embarrass you so easily?'

She dropped her eyes, startled. Why did he say that? How did he *know* that?

'I send you into a tail-spin, don't I?' he went on softly. 'You look at me and I scare you stupid. And maybe you're right to be scared.' He leaned forward suddenly and forced her chin up so she had to look him in the eye. 'Shall I tell you what I see when I look at you?' There was something dangerous in the still voice.

Alexis stared at him dumbly. With his other hand he pushed her hair back off her face.

'Oh, those eyes,' he said as if to himself.

'What?' said Alexis, slightly fuzzy. She wasn't sure she had heard him properly.

'You're a beautiful woman, Alexis Brooke.' He sounded almost angry, she thought, bewildered. 'If you don't want to see it, that's your business. But don't expect the rest of the world to be blind too.'

She jumped, wincing, the strange, mesmerising atmosphere shattered. 'You're crazy,' she said, pushing his hand away.

His face looked bleak and arrogant again, just as he'd looked at Sheila's party.

'Don't you *know*?' Michael demanded harshly. 'Yesterday morning I woke up with you in my arms.' It sounded like an accusation.

Alexis found herself very cold and breathless. 'That was an accident. I wasn't there because you wanted me. You were angry——' She broke off at his expression.

'Oh, I was angry. It didn't stop me wanting you.'

Alexis stared at him, her mouth suddenly dry. Even Patrick had never said he wanted her, never used that hard, self-castigating tone or looked at her as if he would devour her with his eyes. She suddenly realised how very alone they were. Her breath quickened. The silence stretched.

Michael made an impatient gesture suddenly, pushing his hand through his hair. She watched the dark waves ripple and thought, I want to do that. She put her hands behind her back.

'Hell,' he said on a gust of unmistakable fury. Then he was rueful. 'I guess I need to look to my own inhibitions. I never meant to tell you that.'

Alexis went round the table to stand in front of him. Michael stood up.

'You mean it,' she said, amazed, scanning his face.

'Oh, yes, I mean it.' He sounded weary. 'Shall I show you how much?'

She was swaying. Patrick had said she was cold as ice. She had believed him. Suddenly it occurred to her that they might both be wrong.

'Yes,' she said.

CHAPTER FIVE

MICHAEL stood unmoving under her mouth for a moment. Then he gave a muffled exclamation and moved. Alexis felt the slightness of her body in his hands as he strained her to him.

'Damn,' he said with fury. 'I should have known this would happen.' He wasn't talking to her.

Alexis was feeling very strange. The heartbeat under her questing fingers was like a small earthquake, shaking her to pieces. She was reverberating from her head to her toes. Her brain rang with it.

I'll never be the same again, she thought. Her hand curled against the tanned skin, savouring his warmth. And somewhere in the fuzzy shadows her mind said resignedly, I suppose it *had* to be a born again hell-raiser.

His mouth left hers and trailed down her neck. Alexis arched her throat. The world swung wildly. She grabbed at his shoulders, feeling the muscle and sinew under her fingers. She marvelled at it, as if he were an alien. He said something against the tender skin beneath her ear. When she didn't answer he gave a soft laugh and swung her off her feet, one strong arm under her knees, the other round her shoulders.

Alexis gasped and clung to him. His face was very near. It danced before her eyes, out of focus. She shut her eyes.

'Don't do that. Look at me.'

The voice was quiet but it made her quake.

Alexis opened one eye cautiously. The floor seemed to be coming and going. Michael's arms felt like rock but she had the craziest feeling they were about to drown together.

'I'll pull you over,' she said indistinctly.

'You can try,' he agreed, sounding amused and oddly resigned. 'Where am I taking you?'

She had the feeling he had asked the question before.

'My room,' she said, slightly hurt that he needed to ask.

His mouth slanted. 'OK. Map co-ordinates, please?'

She chuckled. 'Due north.' And at the look on his face said hastily, 'Opposite door from the engine-room and up the spiral staircase. It's the fourth door off it.'

They went.

'Your navigation improves on alcohol,' Michael told her, shouldering his way into the room, and kicking the oak door shut behind him. He looked round and whistled softly under his breath.

'Where's your spinning-wheel?' he muttered.

Alexis didn't understand him. She looked round, puzzled.

The bed was large and old and heavily carved. The walls were stone, hung with rugs and tapestries she had largely found herself. Her music-stand stood by the casement. The bed had been freshly made and the covers turned down. The air was full of the scent of lavender. It was a room waiting for occupation.

Michael lowered her gently to the bed. Alexis let her eyes travel round, as if she'd never seen the room before.

She thought, I've never brought anyone here. From the quizzical look on his face, she had half a suspicion that Michael had somehow detected the fact.

It occurred to her suddenly that it was strange that she should never have invited Patrick into her sanctum in all the long hot summer when she was falling in love with him. Yet this stranger walked in at her invitation and immediately looked as if he belonged. A stranger, moreover, who was an international heart-throb.

She closed her eyes. 'I must be out of my mind,' she muttered.

Michael was undoing the laces of her shoes.

'Well, at least we've got that in common. Left foot up,' he said. He sounded wry.

He went about undressing her with the efficiency that she realised must be due to long practice. But he seemed surprisingly cool for an international heart-throb bent on seduction, she thought. Alexis opened one eye and looked at him warily.

'If this is seduction, Hollywood style, it seems a bit unromantic,' she observed muzzily.

Michael looked up from his task. His eyes were unreadable. He touched her cheek.

'Hollywood style you would have a man over there with a boom, another one here with a camera. Maybe another operating an overhead camera. Plus the make-up artist, the continuity people, the director and maybe the writer as well,' he informed her drily. 'Believe me, by comparison—you want romance? This is romance.'

Her head was spinning. 'You're laughing at me,' she accused.

'I'm more likely to laugh at myself.' His voice seemed very far away. 'You're powerful magic, Cinderella. I've got a feeling you could turn out to be lethal.'

Alexis didn't understand that. She collapsed among the lace-edged pillows.

'I feel funny,' she said.

'I know.' Was he amused?

'Don't leave me,' Alexis said, assailed by a sudden fear. He hesitated. 'Please.'

She felt the bed give as he sat down beside her. Her hand sought his across the coverlet. She found it and held on tight.

'No, I won't leave you.' He sounded grim, though.
She couldn't keep her eyes open. 'Promise?'

'Promise,' he said. 'I must be out of my mind, too.
But I promise. Do you think you could try going to sleep?
Please?'

Alexis gave a little sigh. Her convulsive grip on his
hand relaxed. 'You keep your promises. You said. You
see, I do listen to you,' she murmured, drifting far out
into sleep.

Her last impression—and one that puzzled her con-
siderably as she drifted into sleep—was that he swore.

The morning brought total recall, of course, and with
it the sort of embarrassment beside which the first occasion faded into oblivion.

'Oh, good grief,' said Alexis, sitting bolt upright, her
hands pressed to her burning cheeks.

She found she was wearing her underclothes and a
silky robe that Michael must have found in the wardrobe.
At some time in the night, too, he had inserted her between the sheets. She looked anxiously round but could
see no signs that he had shared the bed with her.

She got up and staggered. Her mouth felt like sand-
paper and she had an unpleasant reminder of the swimmy
feeling she had experienced the previous evening. It was
not pleasant at all this time, she found. She groaned
aloud.

That did not produce any signs of life. But the smell
of coffee wafting under the door told her someone was
up and refreshment was in hand.

She belted her robe and cautiously made her way down
the stone spiral.

If she had hoped for Consuelo or one of her cousins,
Alexis was destined to disappointment. The only figure
in the kitchen was Michael Slane, incongruously intent
on a percolator. Even concentrated on that domestic task,
he looked dark and dangerous and faintly raffish.

He had raided the wardrobe. Alexis couldn't remember who the plaid shirt had originally belonged to—but it was obviously not someone with Michael's breadth of shoulder.

He looked up when she came in. The look he gave her was a measuring one but he said blandly, 'Good morning.'

Alexis shuddered. 'Is it?'

An eyebrow rose. 'It will be when you've had coffee and a shower.'

She collapsed at the table, her head in her hands. 'I feel like death.'

'That's the hangover,' he said unsympathetically.

Alexis looked at him with resentment.

'I suppose you've had plenty of experience.'

He looked her over coolly. 'Yup. And you'll live,' he told her. 'It gets better when you rehydrate. Have some water.' And he pushed a bottle of mineral water across the table to her.

She unscrewed the top, wincing at the noise it made when the pressure was released. Michael laughed. She poured and drank, ignoring him.

Slightly to her surprise, she found he was right. Almost at once the swimminess and faint nausea disappeared.

'Thank God,' she said devoutly.

'Ham and eggs and a pint of black coffee—that's what you need.'

Alexis looked at him with loathing. He had shaved and evidently showered, because his hair was still damp. He looked fit and alert and ready for anything.

'What I need,' she said bitterly, 'is to rewind the last three days. Or at least the last twelve hours, and lay off that wine.'

He took the percolator off the range and poured coffee into a couple of earthenware mugs.

'I thought at the time you were overdoing it. On top of a couple of bad nights and not a lot of food.' He didn't sound kind.

He brought the mugs to the table. Alexis took hers and sipped moodily. 'How do you know they were bad nights?'

His smile was a blatant challenge. 'I shared them,' he reminded her.

She choked.

'With anyone else,' he went on, 'I'd have refused to open the second bottle. But you were adamant that you could handle any amount of liquor. So——' And he made a crisp gesture with his hands, transferring responsibility for her hangover straight back to her.

She groaned, thinking of what else she had to bear responsibility for. 'I made a real fool of myself, didn't I?'

He shrugged. 'Don't worry about it. Most of it was tiredness and a lot of the rest was down to me.'

Alexis dropped her eyes.

'Don't look like that.' He sounded impatient. 'I knew what I was doing and you didn't. I reckon we got off lightly in the circumstances.'

He wasn't, Alexis knew, talking about the wine or its effect on her. He was talking about the much more potent effect that his nearness seemed to have on her common sense. To say nothing of her blood-pressure.

She said with difficulty, 'I know I behaved badly last night...'

He looked at her as if he didn't believe his ears.

'Behaved badly? What do you think I am, Alexis? Your social worker?' His voice was harsh. 'I wanted you. You'd had enough to drink to think you wanted me.'

She flushed. He watched her.

'As a matter of interest—why was that? You've made it very clear you're not among my admirers. Did you fancy a movie star's scalp after all?'

Alexis winced at the tone. It was honed steel.

She said miserably, 'I don't know. I've never done anything like that before. I mean—I don't...'

She faltered into silence. Looking at the forbidding hawk's face across the table, she found her half-formed idea of telling him exactly how inexperienced she was becoming rapidly less appealing. Michael Slane didn't look as if he was in a mood to accept virginity as an excuse for anything.

'I don't sleep around,' she finished lamely.

'And I do? So it was OK to do your belated experimenting on me?' Michael asked in a dangerous voice.

'*No*.' Alexis was horrified. 'No, I didn't mean that. I never thought that.'

'Last night,' he agreed evenly, 'you weren't thinking at all.'

She shut her eyes. 'I'm sorry,' she said in a strangled voice.

'So you should be. You were let off the hook last night and don't you ever forget it,' he said with a softness that was somehow more alarming than if he had shouted.

She winced.

'And if you offer me an opportunity like that again,' he told her evenly, 'I give you fair warning I'm taking it. So watch yourself, Cinderella.'

Again? Alexis thought of his smooth, warm chest under her hand and blanked out. When she focused again, Michael was talking about the luggage.

'...don't know where.'

She swallowed and took some revivifying coffee.

'No, you wouldn't. Most of it will go in the music-room. That's above the main hall. The bit that runs between the towers,' she explained. 'I'll get dressed and show you.'

She put on her most frayed jeans and washed-out shirt. It would be terrible, she thought, if he suspected how she felt and thought she was trying to attract him. As they carried the books and manuscripts up to the music-room, she kept a scrupulous distance between them.

She thought, from the knowledgeable glance he gave her, that he noticed. But he didn't say anything.

The music-room was a long, high barn of a room. It had been carefully designed with a polished wooden floor and great swaths of crimson curtaining on either side of the floor-to-ceiling windows.

'It's like being in a soap bubble,' Michael said. 'All that light on all sides. The sound's weird too.'

'That's deliberate,' said Alexis, glad to have found a neutral subject with which she was at ease. She still couldn't meet his eye. 'The room was designed to achieve perfect acoustics. That's why voices sound rather strange in here. Unless they're singing, of course.'

He flung back his head and rolled out a couple of lines of 'John Brown's Body' in a powerful baritone. It filled the room.

'You're right.' He sounded fascinated. 'How's it done?'

'It's to do with the resonance of natural materials as well as dimension, I think,' she said with an effort.

Michael, clearly, was having no difficulty in putting last night out of his mind.

'So what does your stepfather do here? Sing?'

Alexis concentrated. 'Oh, no. This is really for re-citals. Singers. String quartets. You know the sort of thing.'

Michael shook his head. 'I doubt it,' he said drily. He jumped up and down on the wooden floor. 'But this is a great floor. It could even be sprung. Ideal for dancing.'

He looked round. 'Does he have parties, your
stepfather?'

Alexis thought of Fred's musical gatherings. 'Maybe
not what you'd call a party.' She looked at Michael ex-
amining the lighting. 'You enjoy them, don't you?' she
said with a wistfulness she was hardly aware of.

He sent her a narrow-eyed look. 'Enjoy? They're part
of the job.' He thought for a moment and pulled a face.
'Hell, partying is a whole profession on its own.'

He sat down on the piano stool, his hands clasped
loosely between his knees.

'I was a poor boy, Alexis,' he said in a voice devoid
of emotion. He didn't look at her. 'I'm not like you—
with castles in the family and fame in the DNA. I wanted
to work in movies. I did what I had to do. I had the
talent and I worked damned hard too. And yes, I partied.
It's in the deal. I'm not ashamed of it.'

She sat very still. She had the odd feeling that he had
forgotten she was there.

'I did stunts. I drove cars. I wasn't afraid of anything.
If they paid me, I did it.' He gave a harsh laugh. 'On
the whole it paid off. I got the breaks. I've been lucky.
Some people do all that and never get the breaks. These
days I write my own contracts.'

He sounded hard and confident. Alexis thought she
heard something else behind the cool certainty, though.

'But . . . ?' she suggested quietly.

Michael sent her an impatient look. 'Want to know
it all, do you? You may not like it, Cinderella.'

He stood up and went to the widow, his hands in his
pockets. He looked out, his back to her.

'The publicity,' he said slowly. 'At first it doesn't
matter. It's a joke. You even enjoy it. It's got nothing
to do with you, the person you really are. Your friends
know that. But that changes. You can't go to a res-
taurant without some guy with a camera appearing. Your

friends aren't comfortable with it. Pretty soon, the only people you see socially are the others on the star circuit. You begin to lose touch with who you really or—or were.'

He turned back to her. 'You asked whether I'd been round the carousel with Rosie Harvey. Well, the papers say I have. I've stopped denying it.'

For some reason that hurt. Alexis reminded herself rapidly that she was immune to Michael Slane. Patrick had given her that immunity. It might, she thought grimly, be the best thing he'd ever given her.

She said sharply, 'Is that how you got to play opposite her?'

His brows flew up. 'Wow. You don't pull your punches, do you? No, honey, that was some of the luck I told you about.' He gave her a wicked grin. 'They were desperate. They were three days off shooting and Rosie had a fight with the guy I replaced.'

'A fight?'

'The real thing,' Michael said coolly. 'Plates flew out of windows. Knives were found buried in cushions. They were masking out her bruises with make-up for a week.'

Alexis gasped. 'He *hit* her?' Unconsciously, she hugged her wrist to her.

His eyes narrowed. But he shrugged. His voice was dry. 'And that's nothing to what she did to him. Jack had to have stitches. His agent threatened to sue. There was no question of their working together after that.'

Alexis was repelled. 'What were they quarrelling about?' she asked, trying to disguise it.

'Billing,' he said. 'The size of their names on the poster.'

She stared at him in disbelief. His mouth crooked at her expression.

'If you're ambitious it's crucial,' he told her. 'I've felt pretty murderous in my time about billing. On that occasion, of course, as an unknown I wasn't even in the race.'

Before she thought she said, 'Was that why——?' and bit it off a second too late.

But he wasn't offended. The brown eyes gleamed in amusement.

'You learn fast,' he said. 'That's why Rosie chose me.'

Alexis remembered the series of slick romantic thrillers starring Rosemary Harvey and Michael Slane. He attracted at least as much media attention as his co-star. The actress was talented and gorgeous but it wasn't her talent that kept the audiences queueing up for more, she thought. It was Michael Slane's and his smouldering air of concealed danger.

She said curiously, 'And she's never regretted it?'

His eyes narrowed. 'You're shrewder than you make out. Sure, she regrets it about twenty times a picture,' he said indifferently. 'But we work well together. Too well in some ways. Rosie and I——' He stopped.

Alexis was rather startled to find she didn't want to hear Michael Slane tell her about his affair with his tall blonde co-star. It was nothing to do with her. He'd stepped out of his world into hers briefly but he'd go back soon enough. In fact, the sooner, the better for her peace of mind.

She went over to the CD shelves and began to flick through the catalogue, not seeing the titles.

She said, 'You must want to get back. It's easy to get a flight at this time of year.' She could hear the coldness in her own voice and was startled by it. 'Fred has an arrangement with the taxi in the village. They'll take you to the airport.'

He said harshly, 'If you think I want to get back to Rosie Harvey, forget it.'

Alexis said with her back to him, 'It's nothing to do with me whom you want to get back to.' It sounded waspish. '*I* don't care.'

There was a quick movement behind her. She turned but he was already upon her, his face set in forbidding lines.

'People who don't care,' he told her, watching her mockingly, 'don't ask.'

Alexis blushed furiously. 'I didn't. I——'

'And people who don't care,' he went on ruthlessly, 'don't try to get rid of help when they need it.'

'I don't,' she said between her teeth, 'need your help.'

She was horridly aware that she sounded shrill. It didn't endear Michael Slane to her. She never behaved badly; never lost control and shouted at people. Even when Patrick had put his hand on her shoulder and...

Alexis blanked that memory out fast, as she had blanked it out so often in the last eight weeks. It horrified her that it had come so close to the surface. And when she wasn't even alone. She knew she'd lost colour. She hugged her wrist.

Michael had seen it. She saw the way the brown eyes sharpened. She tensed.

He said casually, 'How come you broke your wrist in the first place?'

She froze, transfixed. Then she began to shake. She saw him notice that and felt sick. She said breathlessly, 'I fell.'

'How?' It was very quiet, almost as if he weren't really interested. But Alexis wasn't deceived.

She said hurriedly, 'I didn't notice where I was going. I—I slipped over in a practice-room at college. It's a parquet floor and...'

'So who was with you?'

'...they'd polished it more than usual.' His question brought her tumbling words to halt. 'What?'

'Who was with you?' he repeated quietly.

How, thought Alexis, *how* had she given herself away? Nobody else had asked her that. Not the sister at college when she'd clearly needed hospital treatment; not the dean when she'd reported the accident to him in person. Not Fred. So why did Michael Slane look at her and realise that the injury was not all it seemed? And it wasn't the first time he'd done it, either, she realised it with a little jolt of shock. She shut her eyes.

'Who?'

He was coming towards her. As if it would ward him off, she said swiftly, 'My composition tutor.'

'Who is?' asked the implacable voice.

Alexis moistened her lips. She felt as if she were giving evidence. Or on trial herself. She glared at him. But something in the dark eyes made her own fall.

'Dr Montague,' she muttered. 'The name won't mean anything to you. He's—he's just starting really. He's only had a couple of commissions...'

'And this guy who's only had a couple of commissions teaches you?' Michael said sceptically. 'I may not know much about music but I sure as hell know the way the world works. Your stepfather is a big cheese on the classical circuit and you're taught by a nonentity? What gives?'

Alexis winced. He could have been talking to Fred.

'Patrick Montague?' her stepfather had said. 'For *composition*? You can't be serious.'

She said angrily, 'He's not a nonentity. He's very talented. I *chose* him. I'm very lucky to have him as my tutor.'

Brown eyes that were horridly shrewd searched her face. There was no doubt he saw the defensiveness, the defiance. But Alexis couldn't guess what conclusions he drew from that. She had a nasty feeling, though, that she had told him a lot more than she wanted to. And certainly a lot more than anyone else knew except Patrick himself.

Michael said almost idly, 'And what do you do in these classes? Sit at a desk and answer yes or no? Trip up to the blackboard?'

Alexis relaxed a little.

'Oh, no. Sometimes we sit at the table but normally it's at the piano. There's just the two of us——' She broke off. Too late.

'Just the two of you? At the piano?' He was gently satirical. 'You don't play it standing on your head, I guess. So you didn't fall over at the piano. Where *did* you fall, Alexis? And where was Dr Montague when you did it?'

Her eyes widened. She stared at Michael. She could see herself in the floor-length mirror at the end of the room, small in her tattered jeans and white to the lips. Her mouth was dry. She was shaking convulsively.

She hugged herself harder but it made no difference. Nothing could block out the terrible shock, the sense of betrayal and, too late, fear.

She'd been oddly reluctant to show Patrick the new work. It had been there for months, since the start of the year really, when she'd first decided she wanted to take up composition. She'd chosen the course and she'd chosen Patrick and yet—somehow—she hadn't wanted him to see the concerto. She'd told herself it was beginner's nerves. She'd made herself take it in that day...

His reaction had been worse than she could ever have imagined.

She was a vain fool, a child, he had stormed at her. He was shaking with rage. She was a spoiled princess. If it weren't for her dead mother's fame, her stepfather's influence, no one would ever have taken her seriously. Her talent was tiny. She shouldn't run away with the idea she was anything special. And then the cruel words didn't seem as if they were enough for him, and he had struck out at her, flat-handed and vicious.

No one had struck Alexis in her life. She hadn't seen it coming. She couldn't have been more appalled if the music-stand beside her had turned into a cobra and spat its venom into her eyes. She had gone down once, clumsily, her left hand wrenching agonisingly under her as she fell.

Immediately he had been all contrition. But by then Alexis was too stunned to pay attention.

And now the ravages of that terrible interview were there in her face. She could see it reflected in Michael's expression.

He said quietly, 'He hit you, didn't he?'

'How——?' It was as good as an admission.

There was a silence in which Alexis thought she could hear the motes of dust ricochet off her skin. He looked formidable and tough and he felt as if he were her enemy. She took a step back and found herself up against the crimson curtains. His mouth twisted a little as he registered her retreat. But he didn't follow her.

Instead he answered the question she hadn't managed to formulate.

'When I told you about Jack and Rosie, you looked sick. And there's been something odd about the way you keep wanting to ignore the broken wrist. I thought that from the first,' he told her in a strangely clipped voice. 'But I guess I really knew just now. When you told me his name. Your eyes changed.'

Alexis was afraid she was going to cry. Instead she said truculently, 'If that's true, why has nobody else seen them change?'

His face went still. 'You mean you haven't *told* anyone?' He sounded as if he could hardly credit it. He read the answer in her face. 'Damn it to hell,' he swore.

And then she did begin to cry.

CHAPTER SIX

TO HER astonishment, Alexis couldn't stop crying. Through her tears she saw that Michael Slane looked harshly angry as she knuckled her eyes. He made a move to touch her—or she thought he did—but then his arms fell back to his sides and he turned away.

Alexis sniffed, trying hard not to feel sorry for herself.

Michael said grimly, 'That's what happens when you repress feelings.' Then, in a fierce voice, 'Don't cry, for God's sake.'

'I can't help it,' she said, hiccuping. 'I don't usually. I'm sorry.'

He said, 'And I don't usually drive women to tears. I——' He broke off, looking down into the courtyard below. 'Visitors,' he said in a sharpened voice. 'Were you expecting someone?'

Alexis went to the window. A small truck had pulled into the paved square. She looked down at its rickety shape and her heart sank. The horn blared. She knew who it was all right.

'Paco,' she said hollowly.

Michael looked down at her, one dark brow rising. 'Not a friend?'

She shook her head. 'Oh, no, he's nice enough. He's Consuelo's brother. He's a sort of head man in the village. It's a great honour that he comes up himself. Normally he'd just send the boy with the groceries. Only...'

'Only?' he prompted.

Alexis gave a rather watery laugh. 'I never know what to say to him,' she confessed. 'He always stays for a coffee and a chat and I—just sit there. I don't know anything about football and he doesn't know anything about music. I feel such a *fool*.'

The tension went out of him. Michael looked amused. 'OK, kid, I'll do the talking,' he said in a Chicago-gangster drawl.

Alexis gave an absent smile, making a valiant effort to pull herself together.

She said worriedly, 'I'd better go and meet him. Oh, and I must look a *fright*. I'll run upstairs and get a handkerchief anyway.' She made a vague gesture round the music-room. 'Make yourself at home. I won't be long.'

The horn blared again, insistently. Alexis took to her heels.

In her lavender-scented bedroom she hurriedly splashed water from the bottle by her bed on to her pinkened eyelids. Then, squaring her shoulders, she ran lightly down the spiral staircase. Only to stop dead when she went into the kitchen.

Paco was indeed unloading his cardboard cartons of groceries—helped by Michael Slane, movie star and idol of a thousand fans. Alexis gaped at them.

Michael had rolled up the sleeves of the borrowed shirt. His muscular forearms were as brown as Paco's and probably stronger, she thought. He was certainly carrying the laden boxes without signs of effort. He was even talking to the other man in deeply accented Spanish.

When she came in he looked across the kitchen at her. He took in her startled expression and a look of profound amusement came into his eyes. He said something to Paco, which she didn't catch, and nodded in her direction.

Paco Gonzalez saw her and at once launched into the sort of speech of mingled exclamation, question and welcome which made Alexis's head thump as she tried to untangle it. She gave him a nervous smile.

'Hey, there,' Michael said in Spanish which even she could understand. 'Slow down, friend. You've lost her.'

Paco gave him the sort of easy grin that he would never in a million years have given Alexis. He also, to her eternal gratitude, slowed down. She sent Michael a respectful look.

Paco explained what was in the various bags and boxes. Consuelo had apparently been very precise in her instructions before she went off to see her daughter on the coast. Alexis, appalled, thought he had brought enough for a siege.

But it was only the staples for the house party, Paco explained, unloading flour and sugar and rice with a practised hand. He had brought enough olive oil for the week only—and he produced a plastic container of what looked like a couple of pints of the stuff. Alexis thanked him faintly.

He explained the rest of the stores to her; put much of it away; accepted coffee from a now openly laughing Michael; insisted on showing his new friend where the wood was stored and how to deal with the emergency lighting; and finally swept off in his truck with much friendly trumpeting of the horn.

Alexis sank limply on to a kitchen chair. Michael looked down at her, laughing.

'What are we going to do with all that *food*?' she said.

'I told you. Have a party,' he teased.

Her eyes went over him like flame-throwers and he flung up a hand.

'All right. All right. We'll put the perishables in the freezer and hope the rest gets used up next week. That *is* when they come?'

'Yes,' she agreed. 'Starting on Sunday, I think. Consuelo must have known, though. Why on earth did Paco bring it all up here *now*?'

'I gather,' said Michael, his drawl very pronounced, 'that it is inconceivable that you and I would be here on our own.'

Alexis stared at him in bewilderment. 'But why——?' She broke off abruptly as an explanation presented itself. 'Oh,' she said, flushing.

He grinned. 'They think you're very sweet and old-fashioned. Paco—is that his name?—Paco was more or less congratulating me on my luck.'

'*Oh*,' Alexis said again in a very different voice. 'Oh, how dare he? How dare you? What did you tell him?'

Michael laughed aloud. 'You wouldn't like it if I told you,' he said, shaking his head. Alexis began to rise. 'That we got here yesterday and you were very tired,' he said rapidly.

She subsided. 'I suppose that's true enough,' she said grudgingly. She glowered at him, feeling rather foolish. 'Why do you always manage to put me in the wrong?' she complained.

He gave a soft laugh, not unkindly. 'Well, you can't be right all the time, no matter how sweet and old-fashioned you are. It isn't good for you.'

Alexis, who hadn't really recovered from her unexpected burst of tears, thought wistfully of flinging her head back and screaming. But in the end she smiled sweetly at him and thanked him for his advice.

'Think nothing of it,' he said courteously, though with a suspicious twinkle. 'Now you were going to show me the rest of this pile. And then you'd better tell me what we have to do to make it ready for the others.'

Alexis began to stand up but at this she stopped, startled.

'Tell you . . . ?'

'Or I can use my initiative,' he offered.

She said slowly, 'I thought you'd leave today.'

'I know you did. You made it very clear. You were wrong,' he told her calmly.

Oddly enough, after the way she had fought his accompanying her to Spain in the first place, her first reaction was relief. Her second, almost immediate, was profound wariness.

'Why?'

He didn't answer that directly. 'Are you saying you don't need help?' It was a challenge. 'With no transport but the Range Rover? With those fires to lay—to say nothing of the beds to make—virtually one-handed?'

He looked tough and competent. He also looked horribly determined.

Not quite knowing why she was resisting, Alexis said, 'But your help?'

Michael shrugged. 'Why not?'

'But—no one will know where you are.'

'An irresistible attraction,' he said lightly.

Alexis looked at him. The brown eyes were limpid. She thought, There's something he's not telling me.

The castle had no terrors for her, in spite of its size and medieval aspect. She would not have minded being there alone or preparing the rooms for Fred's guests in the ordinary way. But she knew how vulnerable her weakened wrist made her and she had not looked forward to straining it to its utmost, as she would undoubtedly have had to do.

And yet... and yet...

'I wish I knew——'

'Yes?' Michael prompted her. The hawk's face was intent.

Alexis gave a little shiver. 'I wish I knew why you want to stay,' she said slowly. 'Why you really want to, I mean.'

His expression didn't change by a flicker.

'Wouldn't be good for you.'

Not for the first time she wished she knew more about the world he came from. There was something he wasn't telling her, she was sure. Was it a woman he wanted to avoid? Or to intrigue? Or was it some legacy of the hell-raising?

'I'm serious. You're holding out on me.'

He shrugged, his eyes guarded. 'Why can't it be the pleasure of your company?' he drawled.

She gave up, laughing aloud at that. 'All right. You're not going to tell me. I won't push any more. I'll be grateful for whatever help I can get. Your reasons are your own.'

He made another of those quickly stilled movements when she thought he was going to touch her, but stopped himself. It disturbed her, even though she was immune. There was no point in playing with fire, Alexis thought; and Michael Slane was definitely incendiary to the female imagination.

She drew away unobtrusively. Not so unobtrusively that he didn't notice, she saw. She flushed faintly. He must think she was a complete idiot. It wasn't as if he would have laid a hand on her if she hadn't thrown herself at his head that first evening, she knew. He'd more or less told her so. And what was it Sheila had said? He only dated stunners? Well, scraggy redheads wouldn't qualify. So she could just stop stepping round him as if she expected him to jump on her at any moment, Alexis told herself.

'Come with me, then, and I'll give you the tour,' she said as lightly as she could manage.

Michael watched her expression. He seemed about to say something. But then he stopped. He shrugged, his mouth tightening, and bent his head in agreement.

They went the length and breadth of the castle; up all four turrets, with their luxury bedrooms and bathrooms designed, as Michael said, for one of the more opulent Chinese emperors; through the library and study and the big rehearsal-room; through the cellars; into the stables and the gardens, and then the fields beyond.

It took the rest of the morning. The sun was high when Michael eventually called a halt.

'OK. OK. Give me a compass and a clear night and I'll find my way round the place,' he said drily. 'I've got the picture.'

He turned and looked back at the castle. He shook his head in mock disbelief.

'It's no cosy beach house, that's for sure. Your step-father has an original taste in vacations.'

Alexis laughed. 'Oh, it isn't a holiday home. It's where Fred comes to work. Or sends other people to work,' she added mordantly.

Michael dropped gracefully among the waving poppies and borage and hugged his arms round his crossed knees. He squinted up at her.

'How come?'

Alexis seated herself more cautiously, careful not to touch him. She tucked her legs under her and plucked a length of grass. She began to trace patterns on the ground with it.

'Oh, when people need peace. To practise maybe. After an accident, say,' she said levelly.

Michael's eyes sharpened. 'Like yours?'

He was too quick. She should have got used to that by now.

'Possibly,' Alexis agreed, her face stiff. She did not look at him.

'So he may have got you out here deliberately?' Michael mused. 'Not to make beds and lay in firewood, but to practise. Practise what? Piano?'

Alexis gave a shaken little laugh.

'More likely to write,' she said involuntarily.

Michael stopped hugging his knees and swung round on her.

'You *write*?' His expression was forbidding suddenly.

'Music,' she supplied quickly. 'Not words.' She added comfortingly, 'I'm no journalist. I told you. You needn't worry.'

It was his turn to laugh.

'Yes, I'd really be in a mess if you were, wouldn't I?'

'You don't sound very concerned about it,' Alexis said, perversely annoyed that he didn't see her as a threat.

His smile was slanted.

'I'm not. You're forgetting your eyes,' he said obscurely.

Alexis debated demanding an explanation. On balance she decided against it. Experience was beginning to teach her that in the sophistication stakes Michael Slane was several leagues ahead of her. And natural wariness warned that there were subjects best avoided unless she was prepared to go a long way further in self-revelation.

He seemed to shake himself out of some reverie. He leaned back on one elbow among the grasses and looked up at her.

'So what does your stepfather think you ought to write while you're here?' he drawled.

Alexis bit her lip.

'If he does, he's the only one,' she muttered at last.

The strongly marked brows rose in swift surprise.

'Tell me,' he commanded.

But she shook her head. The long red hair swung with the intensity of it. Michael watched, his expression difficult to read.

At last he said, 'You know, you're a real contrary lady.'

She flashed him a startled look. 'I don't see why,' she defended herself.

'No?'

He lay back, his hands behind his head, and gazed dreamily at the sky. Alexis watched him for a few moments in considerable irritation. He sounded as if he weren't in the least bit interested, she thought.

'What do you mean?' she demanded at last.

'Mmm?'

'How am I contrary? Why do you say I'm contrary?'

He stretched lazily.

'Oh, because you'll do what you *don't* want to do and you won't do what you do want to do,' he said at last. The undertone of amusement was all too plain.

Alexis took a minute to work it out.

Then she said sweetly, 'How clever of you. I suppose *you* know what I want to do?'

He sent her a dark, ironic look.

'I could make a fair guess.'

She almost ground her teeth. Remembering that it would count as a victory to him, since his teasing was self-evidently deliberate, she stopped herself just in time. She met his eyes defiantly.

'Well?' she challenged him.

The beautiful mouth quirked. 'You were ready to drive the monster to Spain. You let me come with you. You didn't want to. But you did. You fight and resent it but you still do it.' He gave her that lop-sided smile that made thousands of female hearts turn over. 'But I'm willing to bet that inside there's a whole different Alexis, wanting and wanting and not daring to take the risk of saying what she wants.'

She felt almost mesmerised. She stared down at him. Her anger disappeared like morning mist. The air was very still.

He reached up a lazy hand and just touched her face, turning it towards him.

'Isn't there?' he insisted softly.

She shook her head, bewildered.

'Oh, yes,' he said. 'You can run away from it. You can run away from all of us, including that tutor of yours. But you can't run away from that Alexis in there.'

And he ran his thumb with incredible gentleness along the tender skin under her eyes. He looked into her eyes deeply as if he could see her very soul laid out for his inspection.

Alexis was not quite frightened by that steady look.

'You don't know me,' she protested. But it lacked conviction; even she could hear it.

Michael smiled. 'Don't I?'

Alexis felt that the solid hillside on which she was sitting was beginning to turn into cloud and change shape. She put her palms down hard on the rocky earth and pressed until the little grains of earth dug into the soft skin. It would be all too easy, looking into the depths of those unreadable brown eyes, to spin off on some fantasy journey. Her breath quickened.

'Three nights together,' he said musingly. 'To say nothing of a king-size hangover this morning——'

'Don't!' said Alexis, wincing. 'And they weren't nights *together*. Not like you mean.'

'I reckon I've got closer than any other man,' Michael went on, ignoring the interruption. 'And I reckon you're running away from something.'

He sat up suddenly, startling her.

'This accident to your wrist? Does it mean you'll never play again?' he demanded. 'Is that why I haven't heard you practising?'

'No,' she said. 'No, they say I'll play.'

He looked at her keenly. 'So it was a possibility?'

Alexis felt sick with remembered panic. 'For a while. It—they couldn't tell till it came out of plaster. But they say it should be all right. I just don't know whether I can get it back. I've got exercises, of course. And I play a little more every day. I didn't while we were travelling because it wasn't convenient. And this morning I——'

'Had a crashing head,' he supplied.

'Yes, I suppose so,' she admitted, shamefaced. 'But I will this afternoon.'

He laughed. 'I'm not your conscience. Do what you want. What do you play?'

'Flute,' Alexis told him. 'At least that's my main instrument. I play the piano as well, of course. I can manage most keyboards really.'

'Talented,' he approved, his eyes dancing.

'What about you? You played in one of your movies, didn't you?' she remembered.

'I roll a mean drumstick,' he said. 'And I went through the usual guitar stage. But I wouldn't like to do it in front of a professional musician.'

Alexis sniffed. 'Unemployed professional musicians don't count.'

'Ah,' he said. Suddenly his eyes were cool and assessing.

She had a sudden unnerving feeling of having revealed more than she'd intended.

'So what's the problem? Why unemployed?'

Flustered, she said, 'Oh, well, I'm not really out of work. There's stuff here and there. And I teach children, of course.'

'Can't sell the stuff you write?' he said with a deceptive softness.

She stopped as if he'd struck her.

'Or haven't you really tried?' he went on, his tone hardening.

Alexis said in a whisper, 'You don't understand.'

'I understand that your stepfather thinks you ought to be writing. And someone—someone you trust—is telling you you're not any good. You don't know who to believe—but none of it stops you wanting to write music, does it?' he said. He sounded almost sad.

Alexis felt her face lose colour.

'How do you know?' she said, voiceless.

His smile was crooked. 'Honey, I've been there,' he said, self-mocking. 'I look into those eyes of yours and it's like a mirror. That's where I was five years ago. And I'm never going back. You——' He stopped abruptly.

Alexis gathered her defences. She drew a shaky breath.

'I?' she echoed. 'I suppose you think that I ought to do whatever you did.'

He gave a hard laugh. 'Oh, no. Not that. Not you.'

'But you think you know what I ought to do, don't you?' she flung at him.

There was a strange, almost dangerous silence. Then he smiled. It was not a particularly nice smile. It looked as if he recognised that she had flung a challenge at his feet—and picked it up.

'Why, yes,' he drawled, and, before her indignation could burst out in words, 'I think you ought to learn to dance.'

Alexis bounced to her feet in fury. She was speechless. He watched her lazily.

'Not at this very moment,' he protested, a gleam in his eye. 'Later. After dinner maybe.'

She stamped her foot. The poppies shuddered at the impact.

'Oh, you're impossible.'

He leaned back on one elbow and laughed up at her.

'And you're a gift. Have you always had this short a fuse?' he asked, interested. 'Or is it only with me?'

'Nobody else,' she said between her teeth, '*tries* to wind me up the way you do.'

Michael came lithely to his feet, 'Then they're missing out,' he murmured.

There was a tense silence while Alexis fought a childish impulse to slap him. It was alarming. She sould not remember having felt like that since kindergarten. Then her sense of humour reasserted itself.

'You're certainly getting a free cabaret out of me,' she said ruefully. 'The last time I flew off the handle this regularly was when Simon Gilbert used to dip the end of my plaits in poster paint at baby school.'

Michael's shoulders shook. 'Plaits,' he said thoughtfully, his eyes on the auburn hair falling like silk over her shoulders.

Alexis flung up a hand. 'Don't. Whatever you were going to say, don't. I've had all the teasing I can take today.'

He smiled down at her. 'Not a word,' he promised. 'At least not if I get fed.'

Alexis looked at the high sun. The sky was a cloudless blue and the air was humming with warmth.

'Oh, goodness, yes,' she said. She hesitated. 'What about a picnic?'

Michael's eyes glinted. 'Here?'

'If you like,' Alexis said, a little surprised. 'But it's nicer a bit further up. There's a path that isn't too difficult. I usually load up a carrier bag, take a book and spend the afternoon. It's easy enough to take cheese and salad and bread, stuff like that. Would that be all right?' She stopped, with an enquiring look.

Michael had thrown back his head and was laughing uninhibitedly. It seemed to Alexis that the sound bounced off the distant peaks and came back to them. He stopped, choking.

'Honey, the picnics I'm used to are served by waiters to people sitting round swimming-pools,' he said when he could speak. 'Carrier bags and a book are strictly a new experience.'

'Oh.'

He took her hand. 'I'm all for new experiences. Let's go for it.'

A little tremor shook Alexis at that casual, friendly touch. She tried hard not to look down at their clasped hands. Her mouth was dry. She drew a shaky breath and made a valiant attempt to keep the conversation on track.

'Well, I can't offer you a swimming-pool but there's a river of sorts. We could swim,' she offered.

Unseen, his forefinger was circling the inside of her palm in a lazy, intimate rhythm. Alexis swallowed hard. Michael didn't seem to notice. He was looking up at the peaks assessingly. They were still capped with snow.

'And the water's icy, right?'

She chuckled, though the hidden caress was sending small shock waves through her bloodstream.

'Bracing,' she demurred. 'Invigorating.'

'Icy,' he agreed. 'OK. You feed me and I'll risk it. And you can deal with the consequences.'

She laughed. 'It's a deal.'

They went to her favourite place in the whole region. After picking up their rudimentary picnic from the ingredients that Paco had brought, Alexis led the way out of the formal garden, through the olive trees and up a stony pathway. It was overhung by prickly bushes and outcrops of rock.

Alexis went up with the speed of long familiarity, balancing with a hand against a tree-trunk here, a boulder there. As they climbed they could hear the sound of water in the distance.

The sun was high. In spite of the earliness of the season the air was hot. White dust spurted from beneath Alexis's shoes as she pivoted to look down at him. The scents of rosemary and wild thyme caught at the throat. Michael shook the wavy hair out of his eyes and smiled blazingly up at her.

Alexis felt her treacherous heart accelerate.

To cover it, she said briskly, 'Just one more climb. How are you doing?'

He grinned. 'I'll recover.'

The brown eyes had gold flecks in them. She hadn't noticed before. But in the brilliant sun they were the colour of autumn leaves—deep and complex and shot through with gold. They also held an expression which made her heart turn over.

She stopped dead with the shock of it. His smile grew.

'Good,' she said, distracted.

Deliberately, she turned her shoulder, hiding her shaken expression. She turned back to the path. What's happening to me? she thought, trying to calm her racing pulse. He's a stranger. A tough, clever, too perceptive stranger.

All right, he had that effect on thousands of women to whom he was a stranger. She wasn't an idiot. Innocent or not, she could recognise attraction when she saw it. Michael Slanc was compulsively attractive, with his hawk's face and those intent, unreadable eyes.

Attractive—and frightening. Toiling up the path, Alexis thought, He feels like an alien—as if he was born in a different world from me and he doesn't know how I work. He's interested; he wants to know; but he doesn't see me as a person, just an object lesson. And I——

Her thoughts broke off. Yes, how do you see him, Alexis? she asked herself grimly.

The trouble was that he would say something—or look at her with that disturbing smile curling the long mouth—and she would feel as if he knew her better than anyone and she had known him all her life. Instead of what?

Three days, she reminded herself. It was a little chilling. Three nights, as Michael would had said, and three days: the first by mistake, one travelling and squabbling about the road and the third—— And on the third, she realised, she was taking him to her private sanctuary and telling him things she had thought she would never tell anyone.

With an odd feeling of having burnt her boats, Alexis put a hand on the flat-topped rock which looked as if it was the end of the path, and vaulted over it. Michael followed her.

Her thoughts had made her painfully self-conscious. Not looking at him, Alexis pushed aside some trailing convolvulus and bent to make her way through a tunnel of bushes. She went carefully. It would be terrible if that deadly clumsiness betrayed her *now*.

It was almost completely overgrown since last year— a good sign that no one else had been here. She felt a familiar rush of pleasure at the thought that this was still her private place. She stood upright, maintaining a careful distance from Michael, who had followed her.

He straightened and looked round. He said nothing. Alexis stole a look at him. He said in a still voice, 'It's amazing.'

Alexis followed his gaze, looking round as if she had never been here before. In the distance there were the high peaks, their summits pale, though it was impossible to tell whether with snow or rock. They were standing on a grassy plot inset among the rocks. It was covered with moss and heathers and trailing convolvulus. It was barred by sharp, irregular shadows from the over-hanging vegetation and was absolutely secluded.

And below the little natural platform ran a small, rapid river. The water cascaded down from the rocks high above their heads and splashed on to the grass at the margin. It recoiled in bright silver splinters of spray. It curled and tumbled round the rocks in its way, foaming a little at the far side but clear and deep and dark where it flowed round the grassy edge of their promontory.

Michael looked round slowly, taking his time in taking it all in. Alexis suddenly had a horrid thought that he might be looking at the scene as a potential setting for one of his action movies.

Her fingers curled into fists at her side. Don't let him, she prayed. Don't let him say, 'This would make a wonderful movie'.

Michael let out a long breath. But when he spoke it was a relief. And a surprise.

'Do you bring your flute up here to practise?' he asked softly.

Alexis didn't realise how tautly she had been braced, as if for a blow. She relaxed now, with a whisper of laughter.

'Sometimes. Why?'

He slanted her a queer, private look, half smiling.

'Because I'd like to imagine you sitting here, playing to the animals and those mountains over there.'

Alexis made a face. 'Not a lot of animals. The odd squirrel maybe. And the mountains are too far to hear.'

He gave a soft laugh, shaking his head. 'You know, anyone would think you weren't a romantic.'

This, Alexis registered suddenly, was dangerous ground. She knelt down and began to unpack the food.

'Anyone would be right,' she said, briskly unwrapping cheese and salad, her head bent.

Michael dropped down beside her.

'It's not fair,' he said, his voice as warm as melting honey with the hint of laughter she would never, now, forget.

'Bread?' asked Alexis, flourishing a knife over the crusty sliver of loaf. 'What isn't?'

'Lonely lady: plays the flute, looks like a dream, doesn't believe in romance. There ought to be laws against it,' he complained.

Alexis froze, the knife in her hand poised in mid-air. He looked at it, one eyebrow raised. After a moment, she resumed slicing a corner off the cheese. She offered

it to him with a little pot of black olives. He took both
with every evidence of appreciation.

At last she said carefully, 'I saw the downside of romance at an early age.'

Michael propped himself against a rocky outcrop and
watched her, the food balanced neatly in his hand.

'How come?'

She looked away. 'My mother was a very romantic
lady,' she said eventually. 'It—didn't make her very
happy. Or my father. Or my stepfather.'

'Ah.' He waited until she had seated herself and taken
her own food before he began to eat. 'I thought it might
be something like that,' he said, with a faint touch of
smugness.

Alexis refused to rise to that one.

'Not a difficult deduction,' she agreed.

He looked at the cheese. 'This is good,' he said, savouring it. 'So what happened? One big disastrous relationship? Or lots of little ones?'

'Lots of big disasters,' Alexis said.

He maintained an interested silence. She sighed.

'My mother was a diva—she had a really beautiful
voice. People used to fall in love with the voice without
ever knowing *her* at all. And she looked gorgeous, too:
dark and voluptuous with wonderful eyes.'

He put his head on one side, looking at her boyish
figure.

'No, not like me at all,' she agreed with the unspoken
comment. 'I'm like my father. He was another scrawny
sparrow.'

He gave a snort of amusement. 'So what was he? One
of her fans?'

'Oh, no. He was an organist. In his way he was as
famous as she was. Just not very—glamorous. She did
like glamour,' Alexis said, not knowing how wistful she
sounded. 'She'd have loved you.'

'Thank you,' said Michael ironically. 'Pass the olives, please.'

She did. He helped himself to a handful.

He said through an olive, 'So along came the glamorous stepfather,' he said, adding thoughtfully, 'Well, he certainly has a lively imagination. If his interior decoration is anything to go by, anyway.'

Alexis recalled that he had seen the cherubs in their pale blue heaven above Fred's four-poster. A laugh was surprised out of her; suddenly she felt better.

'He was a lot older and terribly distinguished,' Alexis said. 'She was dazzled. For a while.' She stopped.

'And then?' Michael prompted.

Alexis stirred. She took a sliver of lettuce, staring at it with concentration.

'Oh, then she wanted what you call fun,' she said lightly in the end. 'She wanted to forget she was this great star with huge responsibilities. She wanted to go dancing...'

'Ouch,' said Michael under his breath.

'She wanted young men at her feet. She wanted to forget she was old enough to have a teenage daughter.'

'Seen it,' he said. 'So what happened to her? Did she run off?'

Alexis's smile was crooked. 'Eventually.'

'Did you mind?'

She looked away, 'Not really. It was almost a relief. At least we all knew where we were. I never held it against her. She died of some sort of flu; didn't look after herself; didn't listen to the boyfriend of the moment who wanted her to call a doctor...' Her voice became suspended.

Michael reached across the grass as if he would have covered her hand with his own. But he stopped. The strongly marked brows snapped together. He looked down at his hand as if it didn't belong to him.

He said something under his breath. She didn't catch it but it sounded almost angry. Alexis blew her nose hard on a paper napkin.

'Tell me more about your father,' he said. He sounded like a man reading a paper, with only half his mind on the conversation, she thought. 'Another one for dancing through the night and forgetting he has a daughter?' he asked. He still seemed abstracted.

Alexis was shocked. 'Good grief, no. He never lets any of his ladies come between him and his music. I'm not sure he notices they're there, half the time. At least,' Alexis said drily, 'not until they leave and he hasn't any clean shirts.'

Michael shook his head. 'And I thought you were a real spoiled princess. How wrong can you be? You drew a couple of monsters there.'

Alexis shrugged. 'Oh, no. They're very talented, you see. Talented people are entitled to be cushioned; indulged a bit. They give so much and it drains them.'

Michael looked at her sharply. 'You're joking...' He met her eyes and let out a sigh. 'For a moment you had me going there. I thought you meant it.'

'It was the creed I was brought up on,' Alexis said simply.

He stared. No abstraction now. His eyes narrowed.

'You don't believe it,' he diagnosed softly.

Alexis looked away. 'I don't want to believe it. I don't want to be a slave to some egomaniac because he sings divinely. And I don't want to terrorise over anyone else because my talent licenses me to behave badly.' Her voice was quite calm; but there was no disguising the intensity of her feelings. It startled and rather alarmed her.

'Ah,' said Michael, his eyes narrowing. 'Another mystery explained.'

Already shaken by her own revelations, Alexis was in no mood to be dissected by Michael Slane. She was impatient.

She snapped, 'What mystery?'

His voice was a lazy drawl with steel underneath. 'Why you're so afraid to think you might have talent too.'

CHAPTER SEVEN

ALEXIS sat very still. She was shaken to the core.

'No one's ever said anything like that to me before,' she managed at last.

Michael seemed unaware of the extent of her shock. 'Not even the guru?'

For a moment she was confused. 'Who? Oh, my teacher.' She thought of Patrick's most recent comments and grimaced. 'Certainly not.' She paused before adding carefully, 'He's quite clear that whatever talent I had has peaked. It's downhill from now on, according to him.'

'Oh?' He took a piece of bread and put a slice of garlic sausage on it carefully. He sounded almost bored but the brown eyes were shrewd. 'And what do you think?'

Alexis bit her lip. 'Well, of course you're not the best judge of your own abilities, are you? You keep on hoping and...' Her voice trailed into silence. She sounded defensive, she realised.

'So you think you're better than he does,' he mused.

Alexis jumped. 'I didn' say that.'

His smile was slow. 'Honey, you didn't have to. I guess you haven't admitted it to yourself yet. But if you agreed with your Dr Montague, you wouldn't be making all those excuses about not being able to judge your own work. Would you?'

There was no answer to that, Alexis found. She ran an agitated hand through her hair. The silkiness felt slightly damp from the spray of the waterfall. She saw the way his eyes followed the gesture. There was something intent, even brooding about his expression. It made Alexis uncomfortable. Her hands fell like a stone into her lap.

But when he spoke his voice was normal enough. 'What do other people say? Neutral observers?'

She sighed. 'What neutral observers? They're all friends of the family or friends of friends. My stepfather's on the college board. The professor of composition shared rooms with my father at Cambridge. The *News'* chief musical critic was one of my mother's boyfriends. There isn't anyone but——' she swallowed '—Dr Montague who'd tell me the truth.'

There was a long silence.

Then Michael said, 'Wow.'

She was startled. 'What?'

'That's a real castle-sized chip you've got on your shoulder,' he told her, drawling.

Alexis stared. 'What do you mean?'

'Anyone who tells you you're any good is discounted. So anyone who tells you you're rotten must be right.'

'It's not like that——' she began hotly.

But he interrupted. 'Yes, it is. You just told me.'

'You twisted my words. You don't understand.' One eyebrow rose. 'You *don't*,' Alexis said passionately. 'I've had the best teachers, amazing opportunities...all the things your friends on your first movie had. Only they *took* their opportunities. And I've just sat and let them all drift past.'

'Your version?' Michael queried, leaning back on one elbow. 'Or Dr Montague's?'

'Mine.' Alexis sighed again, her anger draining away. She laughed a little sadly. 'My mother used to say I never *cared* enough about anything to do it properly.'

Michael shrugged, reaching for more food. 'You don't strike me as a girl who doesn't care enough,' he said drily.

Alexis passed him the plastic container of olives.

'You haven't heard me play,' she said with wry self-mockery.

The brown eyes lifted swiftly.

'Well, you can play for me tonight,' Michael told her. It was a soft-voiced challenge.

She nearly dropped the olives. Her heart began to beat madly, for no reason at all that she could think of. It felt very like panic. Alexis was ashamed of it. But she was also shaking.

'You don't like my sort of music,' she countered, in a high, breathless voice.

Michael was amused. 'I never said that.'

'Well, then you said you didn't know anything about it...'

'Which will make me an unbiased audience,' he said calmly. 'Won't it? Pass the cheese.'

With a sense of impending doom, Alexis did so. It didn't make it any better that she had brought it on herself.

Although she had played for hundreds of people, almost all of them better qualified to judge her performance than Michael Slane, she realised that she was afraid of playing for him. Afraid that he would agree with Patrick that she was third-rate and uninspired. Afraid that he wouldn't be moved.

'Oh, lord,' she said under her breath.

He pretended he didn't hear that. Instead he settled himself comfortably against the bark of an olive tree and surveyed the landscape.

'Is that river really for swimming in?' he asked.

Alexis did her best to dismiss the unreasonable flutterings in her stomach. After all, he might have forgotten that he wanted her to play for him by tonight.

'Yes,' she said. 'This is the first place it's deep enough.'

He groaned. 'With lumps of snow still in it, no doubt.'

Alexis felt better. She gave him a sweet smile.

'Oh, the waterfall knocks most of those out,' she assured him.

'Do *you* swim in it?' Michael asked suspiciously.

'Every day when I'm here.' Alexis was smug. She didn't tell him she was usually here in late summer.

He groaned again. 'All right, all right. I can see my machismo is on the line here.'

She relented a little. 'You shouldn't swim on top of a meal. Leave it for an hour or so.'

His eyes sharpened. 'Aren't you coming in too?'

She shook her head, her eyes dancing. 'My wrist,' she explained. 'I'm not supposed to get it cold.'

There was an eloquent pause.

Then Michael said, 'I'll keep it warm for you.'

'Oh, but...'

He tipped his head back and shut his eyes. 'Hand in hand into the waterfall,' he mused. 'Stuff of a thousand dreams.'

He reached out a hand and took her wrist. Once again she felt that strange, secretive caress on the softness of her inner arm. She knew she was being teased by an expert. It didn't stop her trembling.

'Not my dreams,' she said firmly.

Up to now it had been true.

'You're not only unromantic, you're a con artist,' he returned cordially, not opening his eyes. 'You want me to go floundering in swift-flowing ice water—on my own—for your entertainment.'

Alexis chuckled. 'I won't tell the papers.'

She followed his example, tipping her head back to receive the sun full on her face. It was as hot as a summer day in London, she thought. Sighing, she let her disturbing thoughts float away. She closed her eyes.

'You'd enjoy it, though,' she said drowsily. 'Honestly.'

She heard him laugh. And then she drifted gently off into sleep.

She dreamed she was standing on a concert platform. It was huge. The lights dazzled her and she couldn't see the audience. Behind her Patrick was at the piano. She wanted desperately to leave the stage but she couldn't see the way out. Alexis felt sick.

She turned to Patrick, hands out, begging him. But he looked through her as if she were made of glass. Someone put a flute into her hands.

A figure came out of the black terror that was the auditorium. He lifted her off her feet and carried her up, away from the flowers and the great shiny piano while Patrick played on, stony-faced.

Then suddenly he wasn't carrying her any more. She was on her feet, facing an audience that was no longer hidden behind the dazzling lights but full of faces she knew—kind faces. She raised the flute. Her rescuer was a rock behind her, his hands on her shoulders. She began to play. She had a wonderful sense of power. Patrick's accompaniment grew louder, angrier. Then it died away.

The applause was like an earthquake. Alexis tried to turn to her rescuer but he wouldn't let her. He was gone.

She ran from one side of the huge stage to the other looking for him. Meanwhile the audience stamped and cheered and urged her to play again. But he was gone and she needed to find him. She was frantic again, clumsy again, bumping into the stands of flowers, feeling their water splash against her...

'Wake up,' said a cheerful voice.

Alexis struggled out of the dream, disorientated. She stared up at the tall figure standing over her. Her puzzled eyes travelled over the broad, muscled shoulders; the smooth brown chest, lifting in deep, athletic breaths; curly hair slicked down and dark with water. Something stirred and uncurled inside her. Then memory returned.

She sat up.

'Michael.' She sounded as shaken as she felt. *Why?* she asked herself.

He dropped down on one knee beside her. One bare leg touched hers, the skin cold but the blood underneath warm and rhythmic. He must have been swimming. He had stripped to his underpants which, whatever colour they might have been to begin with, were now black. He was rubbing a towel round his neck and shoulders. But the spring sun was already drying the diamond droplets on his legs and chest.

Alexis felt her mouth go dry. She moved casually, so that they no longer touched. It didn't make much difference. The electric tingle was still there. *Why?*

His mouth slanted and she knew she hadn't been casual enough.

But all he said was, 'You're right. It feels wonderful. But if you really aren't supposed to get that wrist cold, you shouldn't go in.'

'Chilly?'

'Like diving into a Michael Slane special,' he told her solemnly.

He tossed the towel away and reached for his shirt. Alexis watched, fascinated. He shrugged into it, not bothering with the buttons and lay back with a sigh.

'What's a Michael Slane special?' she asked.

He laughed. 'One part Jack Daniels, one part Amaretto, three parts freshly squeezed orange juice and ice, ice, ice.'

She shuddered. He reached out a hand. Once again he stopped mid-gesture, as if he'd remembered something.

'It's OK. You're let off. I won't throw you in,' he said lightly, his eyes still closed.

Alexis was torn between relief and a sense of disappointment. Had he been going to touch her? And if so, why had he stopped? Because she wasn't a sophisticated Californian like Rosemary Harvey and might read too much into it? It seemed all too possible.

And just as well, too. I don't want him to touch me, she assured herself.

He turned over on his stomach suddenly and grinned at her. 'Don't look so worried. I won't sue.'

The brown eyes were too warm, too close. Alexis felt a strange heat under her skin. The brown eyes saw too much, as well. She scrambled to her feet.

'Maybe a swim would be good,' she gabbled.

He reached up a hand and took hold of her. 'With an injured wrist? Forget it.'

Startled, she looked down at him. He gave her hand a little tug.

'Sit down, Alexis,' he said with determination.

Alexis met his eyes and did as she was told. She sank back on the grass, feeling dazed. She fought it valiantly.

'Who are you to order me about like that?'

'Order? Honey, I'm begging you not to show me up,' he said wryly. 'Think of the fans. Think of my image.'

Her breathing came back to normal, though he was still too close. She put her head on one side and pretended she didn't know he was too close.

'Oh, if we're talking about your *image*...' She made a great show of reluctance. 'All right. If your image is at risk I'll keep out of the water.'

'A grateful industry breathes again,' he assured her.

He propped himself on one elbow and looked down at her. It was odd, Alexis thought, how someone smiling into your eyes made you feel as if they could see all your secrets laid bare. She closed her own, dazzled. No one had ever smiled into her eyes like that before. Not even Patrick.

She felt a hand touch her brow. He was tracing lines across her forehead.

'Don't frown.' It was his husky, teasing voice. 'You'll stay like it.' And he touched a fingertip to her lower lip.

Alexis felt a strange sweet shuddering start inside her. She knew she ought to protest but she felt too comfortable, too relaxed. She gave a little sigh of pleasure and sank back on to the mossy ground. Her eyes drifted open, a question in their depths.

Michael bent over her, smiling. He began to spread his fingers through her hair, watching it fan out across the back of his hand. He looked absorbed. Alexis thought suddenly, He looks *happy*. The little bitter lines at the corner of his mouth had smoothed out. His eyes were lazy and laughing—and something else that Alexis couldn't put a name to.

He bent his head and brushed his lips across her own.

Alexis looked up at him. He was so close, his face blurred in front of her eyes. She had the impression of mischief; and of real tenderness. That would be part of his heart-throb's bag of tricks, she reminded herself, but it didn't have much effect on her uneven breathing.

He touched her cheek, gently pushing a strand of hair away. Hardly aware of what she was doing, Alexis reached up and slid her hands across his shoulders.

As if it was a signal he had been waiting for, Michael caught her up against him. His mouth came down hard and hungry. Breathing was suddenly no longer possible, or required. Alexis lost control.

It was like last night, she thought, half scared at her own daring. Only not like last night, because then she hadn't really known what she was doing and now she knew in every tingling, vibrant cell of her body. His arms were like iron but his mouth was exquisitely gentle. It was she who strained up to him, reckless.

He said her name under his breath. One hand between her shoulder-blades, he caressed her until her senses

reeled. She had never dreamed that a single touch could
burn through her like this.

He went about it slowly, finding the soft skin above
the top of her jeans, below her T-shirt. She gasped. He
bent and set his lips against the slim waist he had un-
covered. She could feel him smiling against her skin.
Then he was tugging at the shirt. As if in a dream, Alexis
lifted her arms and he pulled it over her head.

Then he was kissing her mouth again, his tongue ex-
ploring in a slow, teasing tasting of her. She clasped his
head and kissed him back, while that other wickedly
knowledgeable hand freed her from her clothes. Alexis
hardly noticed. She ached to be close, closer. When he
raised his head she gave a little whimper of protest.

'It's all right,' he said. He was whispering, although
there was no one to hear them. He smiled down at her
again, a little sadly, she thought. 'We've got all the time
in the world.'

He closed her eyes with his kisses. Then, very slowly,
his mouth travelled down her cheek, her arching throat,
her collar-bone. She felt his fingers give a practised twist
between her shoulder-blades and he was drawing her bra
away, never raising his mouth from her skin. Her protest
died in her throat as his lips travelled further. When he
took one lifting nipple in his mouth, Alexis cried out.

Her body convulsed. Her fingers hooked into claws
and locked on to those lowering shoulders. She felt his
breath quicken. Suddenly he was moving against her ur-
gently, explicitly. The careful, contrived caresses were
gone and in their place was an experienced man driven
to a need as sharp as her own.

Alexis recognised the change in him even as she
reached for him gladly. Suddenly he wasn't playing any
more. The fingers that had been coaxing golden spirals
of feeling from her unaccustomed breasts became clumsy,
even a little rough. Alexis winced. But she pulled him

closer. He groaned, turning her head to meet his kiss. She slid her hands under the flapping shirt and ran sensuous fingers down his spine. He drew a sharp breath and broke the kiss.

He bent his head, forehead resting against hers. She could feel him fighting for control. His breathing slowed. Alexis felt the tension flow out of him.

He said in a muffled voice, 'That wasn't meant to happen.'

She pulled her hands away as if they'd been whipped.

'No. No, don't do that.' He raised his head and drew away a little, looking down at her sombrely. He reached for her hand and took it to his lips. 'Don't pull away from me. I never meant——' He broke off.

Alexis turned her head and looked away from him across the tumbling water. If she kept her eyes wide, then he probably wouldn't see the shaming tears forming. Her whole body was screaming in protest.

'To make love to me?' she said in a cool little voice.

'Hell!' For a second he looked murderous. She flinched. 'Don't look like that,' he said in a gentler voice. 'I'd never do anything to hurt you. Don't you know that?'

Don't you think you already have? She didn't say it, but it was there between them, unspoken. He flushed, a dark unexpected smudge of colour along his cheekbones. He swung away from her and hunched his crossed knees in front of him. He looked fixedly out across the water to the far bank.

'Alexis, look. You're very——' He hesitated. 'Young,' he finished.

Unsophisticated, he meant. So she was right. He had turned away because she wasn't Rosie Harvey or somebody like her.

Alexis sat up and retrieved her scattered clothing. She bundled into it miserably, glad he wasn't watching her. She didn't think she could have borne that.

He said in a voice she hadn't heard him use before, 'Alexis, you don't know me.'

She was pulling the T-shirt down over her head. 'I don't know what you mean,' she said through its folds.

Michael made a helpless gesture. 'Sweetheart, you were ready to make love with me just now. And how long have we known each other? It isn't me—don't you see? It's the old publicity machine: Mickey Slane, the Slayer, every woman's dream for a one-night stand—or an afternoon by a mountain waterfall, for that matter.' His voice was raw.

Alexis winced. She was about to deny it hotly—to say she had barely heard of the Mickey Slane and certainly never dreamed of a one-night stand with him or anyone else—when it suddenly hit her that that would be the most incriminating thing of all. Because if she wasn't dazzled by the film-star image, what the hell had brought her—as he correctly deduced—to the point of surrender and beyond just a few minutes ago? She shivered at the thought of it.

She had never come anywhere near that extremity of need with Patrick. And she had thought she loved him. He had certainly been as urgent as Michael—more persuasive in some ways. He had probably wanted her more. And yet she had held on to her sanity and her impulses and reminded them both of his wife and family.

She dropped her head in her hands. 'This is a nightmare,' she muttered.

'Don't say that,' Michael said swiftly. 'It's my fault. I knew what I was doing—my God, I ought to by now— and I let myself get carried away. I'm sorry. But nothing happened and you're OK.'

Nothing *happened*? Alexis turned away and got to her feet. She hadn't realised it was possible to hurt so much.

'"All's well that ends well", in fact,' she said in a sharp, cold little voice. 'And just as well you stopped when you did because I think it's going to rain.'

Michael came to his feet in a lithe movement. He put out a hand. Alexis moved out of range, without acknowledging that she had seen the gesture.

He sighed. He looked up at the sky. The sun was still high but there were black scuddering clouds coming up at a fast pace from the west.

'I think you're right. We'd better get back,' he said.

He pulled on his jeans while Alexis, averting her eyes, gathered up the remains of their picnic.

'Give me that,' he said.

She managed to surrender the bag into his hands without so much as their fingers brushing. His smile was crooked but he said nothing, letting her go fast down the path back to the castle.

They were almost there when they saw another couple climbing the path towards them.

'I thought you said the waterfall was your private place,' Michael said in her ear. 'I didn't realise we might get interrupted.' The amusement was back. This time Alexis found it hateful.

She said curtly, 'It is. But climbers use the path as well. It takes them up to the last wall on the west face.'

'Climbers?' Michael sounded startled.

'It's considered to be quite a good practice climb,' Alexis told him, bridling a little in defence of her mountain.

'I dare say. But in *this* weather?'

The climbers were up to them now. They smiled and wished them good-day. There was a tough-looking middle-aged man and a much younger girl. Both of them had packs with what looked like the full complement of gear. They passed them going at a steady pace.

Alexis shrugged. 'Only experienced climbers have heard of it. They must know what they're doing.'

Michael looked back over his shoulder at the pair disappearing round a curve in the path. 'I hope so,' he said grimly. 'She doesn't look more than about sixteen.'

Alexis stopped dead. For a moment she felt a pang of jealousy so precise that it was like a physical pain. She put a hand to her side. Oh, heavens, how could she be jealous of Michael Slane—who had just made it plain in the clearest possible way that he didn't want her or have any feeling for her?

'What's wrong?' Michael said in quick concern.

She managed a smile. 'Nothing. I must be overtired still. I think I'll have a rest when I get home.'

It gave her the perfect excuse to leave him in the kitchen the moment they got back. He looked at her searchingly. But he didn't try to talk her into staying downstairs with him.

'Shall I bring you a drink later? Coffee or something?'

'*No*.' It was almost a shriek. The last thing Alexis wanted was Michael in her bedroom again.

His eyes were shadowed. 'OK,' he said evenly. 'I'll make dinner since you did the picnic. But don't forget, if you're not down by seven I shall come looking.'

Alexis shivered. 'I'll be down,' she vowed.

CHAPTER EIGHT

IN HER room Alexis moved restlessly among the girlish furniture. She felt somehow uncomfortable. She didn't want to meet her own eyes in the mirror.

What's happening to me? she thought again.

She wished violently that she was back home. For weeks she had avoided going out, seeing her friends. Now she would willingly have gone to orchestra rehearsal just to make the tea and talk to friendly faces. Just to be normal again.

It was because of Michael that she didn't feel normal. Every time she was with him, the feeling got stronger—as if she was waiting for something to happen. As if she couldn't escape. As if, for all her uneasiness and trepidation, she didn't really want to.

'This is crazy. What am I waiting *for*?' she asked the wash-stand. She didn't like the answer that presented itself. 'He's already touched me,' she said, as if she were one half of an argument, answering the wordless opponent. 'Kissed me. Do I want *more*?'

No, said her principles, her common sense and her instinct for self-protection.

Yes, said her emotions.

Alexis closed her eyes. 'I can't stand this,' she said out loud.

But there was no divine intervention and she lacked the courage to go back downstairs to the kitchen and face Michael with her dilemma. So in the end she flung herself on the bed and fell eventually into a troubled doze.

She was awake in good time to forestall his threat of coming to fetch her, however. She showered quickly and got into the most conservative clothes she had in the castle—a dark full-length skirt and a high-necked Edwardian cotton blouse with pearl buttons down the front and small frills at the throat and wrists. She brushed her hair until it shone as if it had been polished. Then, armoured in white embroidered cotton, she went downstairs.

Michael had changed too. He was wearing dark trousers and a pale shirt—cream or a very light yellow— with the sleeves rolled up to his elbows. They revealed tanned and muscular forearms. Once again Alexis was reluctantly reminded of his strength. She felt a little shiver clutch somewhere in the pit of her stomach, and was furious.

She must have made some sound because he turned round. His eyebrows went up when he saw her.

'Very formal.' He sounded amused.

'You said you wanted me to play for you,' she said swiftly.

Michael turned and faced her, his eyes going up and down her body in one comprehensive look.

'You play better in camouflage?' His voice was derisive.

Her chin lifted a fraction. 'I do everything better when I'm properly prepared for it,' Alexis said firmly.

He gave a soft laugh. It made the internal shivers a bit worse. But fortunately he didn't seem to realise it. He shrugged and picked up a bottle, holding out a glass to her.

'Rioja again? Or do you want sherry?'

'Nothing,' she said at once.

'You don't have to repeat last night's excesses,' he said drily. 'Just keep me company.'

But she shook her head. 'It messes up my sense of pitch,' she said. It was true, which helped. 'Perhaps later. If you're serious about my playing for you, that is.'

'Oh, I'm serious,' said Michael. His face looked oddly grim.

Alexis swallowed. 'All right. After supper.'

He poured more wine for himself and took a long draught, watching her over the rim of the glass.

'Why not now?' he asked softly.

At once she was flustered. 'I didn't think... Supper... I mean surely you'd rather eat ...'

He said drily, 'We won't discuss what I'd rather do, I think. And supper is a casserole. It can cook as long as we want. I vote for now.'

Alexis felt sick. He gave her a sardonic smile.

'Look on it like this: my way you get it over sooner.'

Mouth dry, she nodded.

'Where is your flute?' he prompted. He was gentle but quite implacable.

She muttered, 'In the salon.'

'Then let's go,' he said.

He gathered up his wine and the bottle in one hand, opening the door for her with the other. Alexis tried to calm herself. Why on earth she should panic, playing for one uninformed man when she had been playing for experts for years, she could not imagine. But her stomach was turning and turning and her finger-ends were unnaturally cold.

Their heels, his and hers both, echoed like a drumroll in the high room. Michael was quite unintimidated. He flicked on a light-switch and began closing the lofty curtains with powerful swings of the wrist.

Alexis set up one of the music-stands with less than her usual efficiency. She brought her flute out of its case, locked it together and set it down carefully. Then she went over to the cabinet, saying over her shoulder, 'Just me and my flute? Or something bigger?'

Michael had closed all the curtains. The central chandelier gave a light that was as strong as day. For some reason the brilliant light high above their heads made Alexis feel very small.

He stood close to her, his shoulder not quite touching hers, and looked at the indexed tapes and CDs.

'Impressive,' he said, the ghost of a laugh in his voice. 'An accompaniment for every occasion.'

Alexis moved away from him, on the pretext of studying the typed catalogue sheet. 'My stepfather prepared most of them. They're not commercially available. At least the tapes aren't. He's done them for various seminars and things he's held over the years,' she explained. 'And I made up some myself when Patrick and I were here that summer I was studying.'

Michael did not seem to be paying attention. He had hunkered down, looking at some of the CDs. He said, still on that thread of amusement, 'He's got catholic taste, your stepfather.'

Alexis had found a piano accompaniment for one of the CPE Bach concertos. She put the catalogue down.

'Mmm? Well, of course, some of this stuff is for his guests,' she said absently.

She found the tape and slipped it into the deck. She switched on, bringing the speakers into the sound system one by one. Michael stood up.

'Do you need any help?'

Alexis looked up. 'Because I'm such a disaster with machines?' she asked.

'I didn't say that,' Michael said quietly.

She shook her head. 'You didn't have to. Anyway, it's not necessary. I've been playing bits of machinery like this since I was so high. It's part of my professional skills.'

She tuned the speakers in carefully and adjusted the higher range frequency. He grinned.

'So I see.' He looked round. 'OK. You do the sound. I'll do the lighting system.'

And before she realised what he was about he had brought the tall candelabras out from behind the piano and grouped them round her music-stand. There were tall white candles in them, ready for the next recital. He brought out a lighter from his hip pocket and flicked it into life.

The irrational tension in Alexis flared at the gesture. She turned away, concentrating on the machine in front of her, though she hardly saw the flickering green lines on the control panel.

Unnoticing, Michael crossed the room and switched off the chandelier. He came back to her, his feet clipping eerily on the wooden floor, his shadow wavering as the candle flames took hold. He took one of the small gilt chairs and set it at a distance from her. A front row of one, she thought. Except that instead of sitting himself neatly, perhaps crossing one leg over the other, he swung it round and sat astride, resting his arms along the frail lyre back, his chin on his hands.

'Ready?'

Did the quiet question mock her? Alexis wasn't sure. She felt even more vulnerable with the candlesticks in an arc around her while he sat in the half-dark. But perhaps it was better this way. At least she didn't have to look into his eyes.

She turned away from the amplifier. Although she didn't need it, she made a great play of setting out her sheet music. It was a familiar gesture and it helped to still her hands. She lifted the flute and played a few experimental notes, then a trill. Then she could put it off no longer.

'Ready,' she said quietly.

She pressed the play button, took her flute and stood, breathing carefully, waiting for the first notes she knew so well.

The deep sound of the piano filled the room. It was a wonderful instrument and Patrick had enjoyed playing it. You could hear it in the way he played. Alexis could remember the day they'd recorded this. It was high summer and she had been falling in love.

Well, she was seventeen and she'd thought they had both been falling in love. Only Patrick had never said anything—except that she was too young to make big decisions. Then he had gone away to the States; and for eight years she had kept the flame of that summer alive.

Eight years, thought Alexis now, as the notes rippled round the room. Eight *years*. When he'd come back to teach at the college she'd thought it was fate. He taught her, he took her to concerts, he took her out to tiny restaurants and held her hand while they ate. He said he loved her. He certainly wanted to make love to her. And it was sheer chance that she had found out about his wife and children before they had.

The introduction ended. Alexis raised the flute to her lips. She forgot the strangeness of the empty room. She forgot Michael. She forgot everything except the exquisitely sad sensation of lost hope and the music that spoke of it.

She had the sensation of the music flowing effortlessly. She had never had it so strongly before. She knew she was playing as well as, or perhaps better than, she had ever done in her life.

When it ended there was absolute silence in the shadowed room. Little draughts stirred the candle flames but were too insignificant to move the heavy velvet drapes. The man astride the fragile chair didn't move. His eyes were intent. They gleamed oddly in the shifting light, while his shadow swayed over the empty floor like a spirit on the edge of existence, trying to take shape.

Alexis lowered her flute and stood with her hands loosely clasped in front of her. She met the shadowed eyes with the fatalistic sensation of facing her captor and her judge.

Eventually Michael drew a long breath.

The tape ended abruptly with a little click that sounded like a pistol shot in the unnatural silence. Alexis jumped. Michael stood up.

He said in a drawl, 'I'd say the guy who said you'd hit a peak was right.'

For a moment Alexis was puzzled. Then she remembered she'd told him what Patrick had said. She smiled but it hurt. He saw that, with his usual acuteness.

'Hey,' he said softly, 'that was meant to be a compliment.'

She turned away and busied herself rewinding the tape.

'Never tell a musician he's peaked, Michael,' she told him lightly. 'It's the end of the road.' She took the tape out and slid it back into its neatly labelled box. 'Now what?'

She turned to face him, brows raised enquiringly. He put his hands in his pockets. There was a brooding expression on his face. His eyes searched hers. She kept her face calm.

'Or would you rather go and eat?' she amended politely.

'What I would like,' he told her, not taking his eyes off hers, 'is to get inside your head and know what you're *really* thinking.'

Alexis shivered. But she put a brave face on it. 'Why?'

He strode up to her, his shadow swinging wildly and then evaporating in the circle of light. He took her chin ungently in one hand and turned her face up to him.

'So cool,' he marvelled. He sounded almost angry. 'Beautifully behaved and ice to your bones. Only your eyes aren't icy, my dear.' He feathered a thumb along her cheekbone, just touching the sooty lashes. 'And nor is your music.'

Alexis thought wryly that she had been as far from ice as it was possible to be on those startling occasions when he had taken her in his arms. A small puddle of warm rainwater was nearer the mark. But she wasn't unwise enough to say so.

'So what happens? Why the character change?'

She jerked her head away from his fingers and took a step backwards. She felt safer with a greater space between them.

'You're imagining it.'

He shook his head. 'No, I'm not. Most of the time you're cool and contained and there's not much on broadcast. Then every once in a while you drop the armour—and you're all fire.'

Alexis retreated another step in pure amazement. She cleared her throat and said unnaturally loudly, 'That's ridiculous.'

His eyes gleamed. He followed her. 'Is it?'

'Yes, it is,' she said hotly. 'And what's more it sounds like a quote from a bad film. I've never heard such nonsense in my life. You don't know anything about classical music at all. You can't judge it on the standards of rock or jazz. It's not spontaneous and emotional. It's—it's built. Like architecture. I don't write it. I just play it.'

Michael said, 'Rubbish!'

'What?'

He repeated it obligingly. 'Are you saying you have no choice how you play?'

'Well, in a way...'

He swept on, over her muttered concession, 'What I've just been listening to was *you*. Not some autopilot.'

'I made more mistakes than a machine would,' Alexis agreed. 'But that doesn't mean the emotion you heard— thought you heard,' she corrected herself, 'was mine.'

She glared at him. For a sizzling second their eyes met and locked. Michael drew an exasperated breath. He pushed a hand through his curling hair.

'You,' he said at last, 'don't know a single thing about emotion. But you play like an angel. Oh, hell, come and eat, before I forget all my good intentions.'

He was in an odd, difficult mood throughout the meal. Alexis, detecting criticism and barely repressed anger, felt her nerves tauten.

Predictably, she reverted to her usual clumsiness. To her acute embarrassment, she smashed a plate, dropped two sets of cutlery and sent a pile of tangerines on a wooden platter tumbling. Scarlet-faced, she dived after them.

'Leave it,' Michael said in a clipped voice. He looked at her searchingly. 'Wrist hurt?'

She straightened, startled. She'd barely noticed it herself. Her eyes fell.

'A bit.'

'Don't look so tragic. Plates aren't irreplaceable,' he said drily. He leaned on his elbows and looked across the table at her. 'Is that why you're so tense?'

'I'm not,' muttered Alexis.

She began to play nervously with the raffia table mat. It was a reasonable excuse not to meet those scathing eyes. She hardly noticed when the mat began to unwind in her hands.

'Then why are you shredding the table furniture?' he asked reasonably.

She looked down and gave an exclamation of annoyance. He took up the goblet she had refused earlier on and poured wine into it. He pushed it across the table to her.

'Tense,' he said firmly. 'You need a drink. Go on,' he urged impatiently, 'it isn't poisoned. And I won't let you get smashed again. I'm not sure,' he added under his breath, 'that my blood-pressure could stand it.'

Alexis flushed. She picked up the wine. Her hand was shaking so much that some of it slopped on to her white sleeve. She could have cried.

Michael reached out for the salt and, without asking her, tipped a generous amount over the red stain. Alexis watched the white grains turn purple as they blotted up the wine.

'Wait till the salt has worked. Then soak it in cold water. You'll have to take it off, of course,' he added drily, as her eyes flew to his in suspicion. 'And then I can get my hands on you again...'

She sprang to her feet, knocking her chair over. Her whole body was one blush. She clapped her hands over her ears.

'Stop it,' she shouted.

'Tense,' he said again. The satisfaction in the lazy voice was blatant. 'I told you so.'

He stood up. Alexis backed away. 'Don't come near me,' she said in a whisper.

Michael's eyebrows went up. 'Now who's talking like something out of a bad movie? What you need is something to do. And as I take it you're not feeling like playing to me any more, I guess I'll have to do what I promised.'

Alexis eyed him warily. He smiled at her, a sudden glittering smile that was like a challenge. She blinked.

'Go and soak the blouse. I'll teach you to dance,' he said. He turned, flinging over his shoulder, 'I'll give you five minutes. See you on the dance-floor.'

Alexis ran to her room and tore off the Edwardian blouse, running the cold tap in her little basin over the stain as she pulled on an old elastic-waisted cotton skirt and T-shirt.

Michael was in the salon. He had lit the candles again, though he had pushed the candelabra all around the hall, which made the shadows enormous. He was crouched in front of the CD cabinet. Alexis hesitated in the doorway.

'It looks different,' she said uneasily.

He came lithely to his feet. 'Sure. It's not a concert hall any more. Come here.'

Feeling as if she were walking a tightrope, Alexis walked across to him. She had put on her favourite old espadrilles, and their canvas soles made no sound on the floor. Michael looked down at them.

'Take them off,' he said, pointing.

Alexis was startled. 'What? Why should I?'

He grinned. 'Because they'll slip. And in the mood you're in tonight you'll break a leg. Probably mine.'

There was so much justice in that that Alexis slipped her shoes off without another word. But the look she gave him was not warm. He chuckled, flicked a switch, and a strong rock beat filled the room. Alexis jumped as if it were attacking her. She looked round a little wildly.

'What on *earth*...? Did you bring that?'

'Oh, sure. I always travel with a disco in my back pocket,' Michael said. He seemed annoyed for some reason. 'It was here. I saw it earlier. There are quite a few. Good old Fred is obviously not as hidebound as you are.'

Alexis saw she had offended him.

'I'm sorry. I've just never heard anything like that here before,' she said.

He shrugged. 'More fool you. It was here just waiting for you.' He came and stood in front of her. 'Now. Tell me. When did you last dance?'

Alexis thought hard. 'Strip the willow,' she said eventually. 'At school. Country dance classes.'

There was a little silence. She couldn't read Michael's expression. But she was pretty sure it was unflattering. She sensed that he was angry again.

But when he spoke it was only to say curiously, 'Surely, with a family like yours, you must go to dances—big things, charity balls, whatever. Don't you dance then?'

She lifted her chin a fraction. 'I've told you. I don't.' She thought of her mother, drifting dreamily round the dance-floor with a young Italian tenor, their mouths all but touching. Alexis had never wanted anyone to hold her like that. Or not until now. Not even Patrick.

She was so startled by the thought that she told Michael the truth.

'There was only one man for me. He wasn't around and I didn't want to—to get involved with someone I knew I'd never commit myself to. So no parties, no dances.' She could hear the pain, though she tried to keep her tones unemotional.

Michael looked down at her thoughtfully. 'One-man girl, huh? No re-runs of Mum's adventures?'

Alexis jumped. There was more than a grain of truth in that. She didn't like it. What right had Michael Slane got to detect feelings that her closest friends had missed?

'If that's the way you want to look at it,' she said coldly.

'Honey,' he said softly, 'I don't have any choice. Most women of twenty-five have done their experimenting. You haven't. I need to know why.'

'Why?' she said angrily. 'What's it got to do with you?'

His look was ironic. 'You really don't know?'

'If I did, I wouldn't ask.'

He put his hands on her shoulders. He held her lightly in front of him. There was no passion there, just that calm, judicial expression.

'This afternoon, if you recall,' he said coolly, 'we came as close as dammit to making love. That's what it's got to do with me.'

Alexis flushed. Her eyes dropped. 'We stopped.'

'*I*,' Michael told her with sudden harshness, 'stopped. You were still mid-experiment.'

'Oh!' She pulled away from the prison of his hands. 'You're not very chivalrous. You weren't involved at all, I take it?' she said with bite.

His eyes were unreadable. 'I was involved.' He looked her up and down. 'And you weren't kissing me like someone you couldn't commit yourself to. I think it's about time you reviewed this one-man woman pose.'

'It's not,' said Alexis between her teeth, 'a pose.'

'Then why aren't you with him?' he said softly. 'Doesn't he want you?'

Alexis thought of Patrick's face, flushed with frustrated passion. She shuddered involuntarily.

'He wants me.'

Michael's eyes narrowed. 'Then maybe you don't want him after all.'

She said, 'It's not like that.' Michael looked sceptical. 'He's married,' she flung at him, goaded.

One eyebrow flicked up. 'So?'

Alexis looked away, the fight going out of her. 'You don't understand. There were children. Patrick said I was being a fool. That his wife accepted the way he lived when he was away from her. But——'

'But you didn't accept it,' Michael said softly.

Alexis thought, He must think I'm prim and stupid. She said miserably, 'That's how I feel. I can't change. People would have got hurt.'

'That's for sure,' Michael said. She was astonished. His smile was crooked. 'You for a start. One-man women want one-woman men, at least in my experience.'

He was pointing out the difference between them, Alexis thought.

'I suppose you think I'm a coward and a fool as well?' she flashed.

He was looking at her, an odd expression on his face.

'No. I think you're very wise. No point in playing with fire unless you want to see how it feels to get burned.' He shrugged, dismissing the subject. 'So you don't dance at all. Back to basics, then.' He held out his arms. 'Come here.'

Alexis didn't move. Michael watched her hesitation. His mouth quirked.

'Afraid?' he challenged softly.

Alexis winced. Why did he always make her feel like a scared rabbit whenever she had a few reasonable doubts about where he was pushing her to go?

She tilted her chin in defiance and said sweetly, 'Terrified. What's it going to cost me in compensation if I *do* break one of your ankles?'

He shouted with laughter. 'A fortune. You'd delay the next movie and destroy my image.' He strolled over to her and put his arms round her quite as if it didn't matter to him. 'Head up and watch where you're putting your feet, Brooke.'

Alexis did her best to suppress the long, sweet shudder that went through her. She felt his palms at her back through the T-shirt as if they had suddenly taken over the function of her spine.

But she said captiously, 'I can't do both without a periscope.'

He laughed again but gave her a little shake.

'Don't make difficulties. And concentrate. Listen to the music.'

The tune was one Alexis vaguely recognised. It had a bouncy, skipping rhythm and it was fast. For a non-dancer it was an elephant trap, she thought.

'Now what you do,' Michael was saying practically, 'is listen to the music till you've got the beat. Then you start to move. Not your feet. Your shoulders.'

His hands in the small of her back illustrated. Alexis swayed in his hands like a puppet, pliant and without will. She felt her hair swing against his cheek with the movement. It was like a caress she hadn't intended. She wanted to do it again, but she repressed the instinctive reaction firmly.

Fortunately Michael didn't seem to notice. She looked at him through half-closed eyes.

'When you've got that, you move with me.' He shook her a little. 'Are you listening?'

A strange languor was stealing through her, utterly at variance with the energetic music. Alexis nodded.

He gave an impatient little sigh. 'I told you: concentrate. I'll tell you when I'm going to start. When I do, just follow me. Keep your shoulders parallel with mine and don't try to do anything clever. Ready?'

Alexis felt a giggle beginning to rise. He sounded like Fred at a rehearsal, she thought. Serious and determined and quite likely to lose his temper. She decided not to tell him that. So she just nodded again.

'Wait for the end of this track,' he said. 'But listen for the beat. That's the first thing.'

The next song was different, though equally familiar in that annoying, half-overheard way. Alexis listened obediently and found the strong, slow rhythm even before Michael's hands began to spell it out for her.

She moved as he instructed. It was easy. When he began to dance her forward and away from his body she went like thistledown, light and confident. The music changed and he twirled her round without warning. To her astonishment she neither stumbled nor stopped dead. It all felt amazingly easy.

'This is terrific,' she said breathlessly when the CD finished.

Michael laughed down at her. 'So you now dance.'

'So I do,' she agreed solemnly. She hesitated and then added with a twinkle, 'Probably not with *everyone.*'

She had been thinking of some of the unsteady elderly friends of Fred's who had asked her to dance in the past. She didn't expect Michael's face to change as if she had said something intimate.

For a moment she held her breath in the charged silence. He held himself very still, like a soldier listening for the enemy. Alexis stared at him, bewildered. Then his hands dropped. He let the tension flow out of him. His face was unreadable. He went back to the CD-player and changed the disc.

This time it was a song Alexis was positive she hadn't heard before. The soft rhythm of brushed drums was seductive. So was the husky voice of the singer. Alexis went rigid. Michael came back to her and took her in his arms.

'Listen,' he whispered.

She stood in the pantomine embrace as if there were a coating of ice over her body that his warm fingers couldn't penetrate.

'Why are the lyrics always such absolute trash?' she enquired in a conversational tone.

His hands tightened. One hand fell to her hip. Michael made her sway with him, their bodies not quite touching. He didn't answer. Alexis felt her mouth go dry.

'Love at first sight,' she scoffed in a high, unnatural voice. 'Ridiculous.'

His eyes glinted down at her.

'You're an expert?' he asked softly.

She tossed her head. Her hair flew against his cheek again, filling her with a sweet secret pleasure.

'I know love isn't some sort of instantaneous madness. If it exists at all,' she said.

'It exists.'

In an abrupt movement he swung her off her feet and pivoted with her, still swaying to the music. When he put her down she was moulded against his body from chest to thigh. He made her keep the rhythm of the song in the small movements their proximity permitted.

'Well, it's not a lightning-flash between strangers,' she said, scorning the song.

'You sure of that?'

Their closeness was a sort of torture. Alexis moistened dry lips. Michael looked almost angry.

'You don't know what you're talking about,' he said under his breath.

And then he began to touch her with a thoroughness she had never imagined in her wildest dreams. He made her keep dancing, but she was his, moving at his instigation in response to his fingers, his arms, his muscular shoulders, the thigh that edged between her own... Alexis began to feel a wholly new species of fear—not of this wickedly confident, wickedly experienced man, but of herself.

He flung her away from him, curving her back over his arm bonelessly. And when he brought her upright it was to meet his mouth.

Something long-buried in Alexis rose, at last. She kissed him back, not in timorous experiment or carried away by fantasy, but as an equal—a hungry, demanding equal.

This time when he picked her up he carried her out of the salon and up the winding staircase without asking. The sound of the song echoed queerly behind them. He didn't take her to her own room but the one he had chosen for himself. Alexis had a glimpse of woven carpets and carved oak furniture and then she was lying on the bed looking up at him in the darkness.

'This time,' he said almost grimly, 'you're going to know what you're doing.'

He took her arms and put them round his neck.

Alexis blinked in the shadows. She felt very strange. She had never done anything like this before and yet she knew exactly what he wanted her to do. She moved slowly, sinuously. His tongue invaded her mouth. But it didn't feel like invasion and she was reaching as avidly as he. Their clothes fell in an unregarded jumble.

His skin under her mouth felt like fire. Michael caught his breath. Alexis felt a glow of triumph. She pressed her open palms against the labouring warmth of his chest and shivered deeply. He was saying her name against her skin, over and over again. His hands moulded her shoulders. Alexis knew she was out on uncharted waters. She shivered again.

'Michael.'

It was no more than a whisper. But it stopped him. He lifted his head, drawing in deep lungfuls of air.

'Darling?'

'Michael, I'm scared,' Alexis confessed, too far out to dare to hide it.

He pushed her hair back from her face.

'Don't be. I'll make you happy, I promise. Trust me,' he told her.

Still Alexis hesitated. She hadn't, she thought wryly, much of a track record when it came to trusting people. She knew what she wanted all right. Her body wasn't leaving her in much doubt about that. But it wasn't enough.

'And you?' she said painfully. 'Can I make you happy, too?'

He touched a hand to her hair, teasing it out strand by silken strand across his pillow. For a moment she thought he wasn't going to answer.

Then he said in a low voice, quite unlike his usual teasing, 'More than you can imagine.'

Alexis took his face between both her hands and drew him down to her.

CHAPTER NINE

ALEXIS awoke slowly. She had a sense that something wonderful was happening. She lay dreamily, feeling sunshine against her eyelids, and thought, Today I'm going to write music again.

Somewhere in the distance someone was whistling. She burrowed into the pillows, unwilling to wake up. But the whistling, though tuneful, was not easy to ignore. She turned over once, groaned and sat up.

As soon as she opened her eyes memory, specific in any number of startling details, flooded back. Alexis looked down at herself and found she was naked.

'Oh,' she said.

She looked round the room. It was one of the turret guest rooms, with one circular wall and its own bathroom set into an alcove. Last night's scattered clothes had gone—though her own were neatly folded on the end of the *chaise-longue* that stood under the window.

Her lips twitched. Who would have thought that the wild Michael Slane had this passion for order? Alexis leaned back, her hands locked behind her head thoughtfully.

After last night, she knew a lot more about wild Michael Slane than she would have imagined possible. She knew that he was patient. And tender. And determined. And when she'd cried out in passion he had held her against him tightly as if she had given him the world.

'Oh,' she said again softly, remembering.

Could it possibly have been mutual? she thought. It seemed incredible. After all, what was an astonishment

144

and a delight for Alexis Brooke was familiar territory for Michael Slane. Yet it had *felt* mutual. Was she being a fool?

The whistling came closer. It brought a smell of coffee with it. She watched the door open and a careful foot being inserted as Michael came in with two fragrant mugs.

He smiled at the sight of her. Yes, it had been mutual. Alexis smiled back. He strolled over, put both mugs down with care and kissed her briefly.

'Good morning. How you doing?' he drawled.

'Wonderful,' Alexis assured him solemnly. 'I'm going to write music this morning. I feel inspired.'

'Great.'

He was wearing nothing but the jeans he had worn at Sheila's party. They sat low on his hips, revealing the sculpted lines of the famous torso that Alexis now knew as well as she knew her own body. She leaned forward and kissed his collar-bone gently.

He mussed her hair and handed her the coffee.

'I hope you take it black. There wasn't any milk.'

Alexis hated coffee without milk. She sipped it and found it had sugar in it, which she hated even worse.

She said, 'Marvellous.'

Michael sat on the side of the bed and tucked one leg under him. He was barefoot.

'Your friend Paco was here. He's brought the post,' he said.

'Oh?' That was a surprise. Fred must have posted whatever it was he wanted her to do before she set off from London.

'You're frowning,' Michael told her softly. 'Don't you want messages from the outside world?'

Alexis laughed a little. 'It's not that. It's just—oh, hell, you might as well know. The only person who knows I'm here is my stepfather. And to get a letter to

me from Japan by today he must have posted it *before*
I said I'd come. So he knew I'd come, no matter what
I said. I'm so *spineless*. And I really did mean to hold
out this time.'

He tucked a lock of hair thoughtfully behind her ear.

'You're not spineless. You're brave and clever and
funny—and sometimes you give a little too much.'

Alexis stared at him. '*Brave*? Me?'

'I'd say so, yes.'

She shook her head. 'You're crazy. I'm the proverbial
timid mouse. I even have nightmares about concerts I
don't have to play in,' she added, remembering horrors.

'But you still go on playing in concerts, don't you?'

She was puzzled. 'Well, yes. I have to. That's my
profession.'

'Not many people,' Michael pointed out gently, 'have
a profession that brings them out in nightmares.'

He kissed her lips with a lingering sensuousness that
set her head spinning.

'Brave,' he said firmly.

Alexis reached for him. But he was already standing
up and turning away.

'Get up and come and eat,' he instructed her. 'As well
as the post, there's the best fruit I've seen since I left
California. And then we have plans to make.'

Alexis raised her eyebrows. 'You're very bossy all of
a sudden. What sort of plans?'

He grinned back at her. 'Wait and see,' he said
maddeningly.

Alexis bounced out of bed, shouting at him. But he
was gone. She could hear him running down the spiral
staircase, whistling.

He was right about the fruit. Paco had brought a
mountain of lemons and oranges as well as small shiny
apples that tasted of winter, and a huge pineapple.

'Forced,' said Alexis with a sniff. But she did not refuse the pineapple when Michael prepared a slice for her and fed it to her across the table chunk by chunk on the end of a fork.

'What's in the post, then?' he asked, stirring the pile of letters with his finger.

Alexis leaned forward, peering. One Japanese postmark. One Austrian postmark. One London postmark. One no postmark at all.

'Fred's last-minute thoughts,' she diagnosed, one by one. 'His even more last-minute thoughts. His agent trying to get in touch with him so sending things off to every address on the filing cards. And——' She stopped suddenly.

Michael looked up. 'Yes?'

Alexis knew the handwriting. Slowly she picked up the long blue envelope without a postmark. How on earth did Patrick know she was here? And how had he sent the letter? She turned it over, hesitating.

Michael said slowly, 'You look as if you know what's in that one.'

Alexis raised her eyes to his face.

'I hope I don't,' she said quietly, 'but I'm very much afraid...'

'Then open it.' His voice was harsh. 'It's always better to know.'

She flinched. She knew he was right, though. She slit the envelope.

It was only a few lines. They said all that was necessary to confirm her worst fears. She let the paper drop from nerveless fingers, looking blindly round the kitchen.

'What is it?'

Alexis bit her lip. 'He knows I'm here,' she said, not very lucidly. 'He's coming.'

Michael's face hardened suddenly. He stood up. 'The infernal Patrick, I take it? The one who hit you? Did you invite him?' he asked coolly.

Alexis shivered.

'No, but——'

'Then write and tell him he can't.'

Alexis ran distracted hands through her hair.

'You don't understand. I don't know where he is. There's no address on this note. It hasn't even been properly posted. He must have left it with the poste restante in the town. I don't know how to get a message to him.'

Michael said something pungent about Patrick under his breath.

Alexis gave a wan smile. 'Yes. Maybe. But he knows I—— He'll think I'll be glad to see him.'

Michael's eyes narrowed. Suddenly he looked like the tough, dangerous man she'd first seen in Sheila Mallory's drawing-room. Alexis swallowed. The transformation was almost frightening.

'In spite of your resistance to having affairs with married men?' he said in a hard voice.

Alexis swallowed. 'He doesn't take my principles very seriously.'

Michael shrugged sharply. He didn't look at her. He looked determined and surprisingly grim.

'Then I'll explain them,' he said softly.

Alexis stared at him, her head whirling. She had never begun to imagine Michael Slane invading her everyday life, meeting Patrick or any of her friends, her neighbours, her stepfather. She did so now in a blinding flash of perception.

All at once she recognised the unwelcome fact that she could imagine it only too easily. Michael would prowl round her unpredictable stepfather, amused and intrigued, until he knew him thoroughly. Unlike most

people, he wouldn't be frightened of him. And, though
he might be impressed by Fred's work, he would be
completely unmoved by the fame or the wayward image.

After that, she thought wryly, they would probably
like each other. They were both originals without much
patience for the conventions. And neither of them liked
other people telling them what to do.

The implication of all this, Alexis realised with a
sinking heart, was that she had somehow managed to
let Michael Slane as close as anyone else in her life. In
fact, thinking of last night with its laughter and passion
and heart-stopping tenderness, probably closer.

She said involuntarily, 'Oh, heavens.'

The brown eyes came back to her at that. 'I told you
I had plans,' he said coolly. 'They don't include the music
man. I shall welcome him, point out that you and I are
alone here together by choice, and invite him to remove
himself tactfully. How does that sound?'

It sounded like the start of a tempest, Alexis thought.
She tried to imagine Patrick's reaction to being told to
go away by a man whom he would with justification—
interpret as having succeeded where he had failed. It
wouldn't be tactful and it wouldn't be pleasant. Patrick,
as she had all too much evidence, had got used to
thinking she was his for the taking as soon as she shook
off her childish inhibitions. Patrick was also quick with
his fists when his uncertain temper was roused.

'Leave it to me,' Michael said.

It was somehow the last straw. Alexis began to laugh.
The sound was on the edge of hysteria.

He leaned forward and took both her hands.

'Stop it,' he said, gentle suddenly, her careful lover
of last night again.

He touched the back of his hand to her cheek. Alexis
hiccuped into silence. He gave her hands a little shake.

'We'll deal with him together. When he arrives.' The voice was low, smooth as maple syrup, but there was a note underneath that was anything but reassuring, Alexis thought. 'There's nothing to get worked up about. Think about this morning. You were going to write music. Do it.'

Alexis hesitated, unsettled.

'Go on, honey. The good feelings are still there, you know,' he told her lightly.

Alexis gave a little laugh that broke. His casualness was devastating, she thought. She was sharply reminded that what might be earth-shattering passion for prim Alexis Brooke might be as ordinary as cornflakes in Michael Slane's Hollywood.

She bit her lip. 'All right. But what will you do?'

He shrugged again. 'There are logs to hew and garbage to get rid of. There are books. There's the view. I might walk down to the village and have a cognac with Paco.'

He tousled her hair; as if she were an urchin, Alexis thought sadly, not his lover of last night, after all.

'I might even cook lunch.'

Alexis did her best with a glimmer of a smile. He looked at her searchingly.

'Sold,' she said with an effort at cheerfulness.

It was a good effort. Anyway, he seemed satisfied.

Contrary to her expectations, the morning went in a flash. She opened the baby-grand piano in the rehearsal-room, set up her manuscript paper and ultra-sharp pencils; and forgot everything.

The first she knew that time had passed was when Michael burst into the room. The brown curls were wildly disarranged. He had clearly been running. He had, she saw with disappointment, put a shirt on.

He said baldly, 'Alexis, we need your help.'

She was already halfway across the room. This stopped her. She thought wildly of journalists and jealous agents.

'What? Who? How?'

But it was none of those things.

'The couple we saw on the way up yesterday. You remember them?' Alexis frowned, shaking her head. 'The old guy and a very much younger woman,' Michael said impatiently. 'Hill-walkers. When we came back from the waterfall.'

'Oh,' said Alexis, enlightened. 'Yes, of course.'

'Well, they seem to have got into trouble. They were supposed to be back in the village last night and they didn't make it.'

Alexis said drily, 'There's a climbers' hut up there.'

'Yeah. They could've decided to make a night of it, sure. But one of the farmboys went looking this morning—just to check—and he says the hut hasn't been slept in for weeks. So they must be out in the open somewhere.'

Alexis shivered. The April nights were not hospitable.

'There was rock-fall, the boy says. During the storm yesterday afternoon. They might have been caught. There's a search party going up. I've said I'll join them.' Alexis's heart turned over. 'You said you knew how to use that short-wave radio set downstairs. Can you get it going? We'll keep in touch best that way.'

Alexis went to him, her hands going round his waist in a pure reflex action. She dropped her head against his chest and hung on to him convulsively.

'No,' she said hoarsely. 'No, you can't. If there's been a rock-fall, it's dangerous. The men in the village—they're the proper mountain-rescue volunteers. They know the country. You don't. You'll only get hurt.'

He detached her hands impatiently.

'I've done a bit of climbing,' he said as if that should have answered her. 'And they're short-handed. I'll do what I'm told, don't worry.' His voice grew bitter for an instant. 'It's only in the movies I'm a hero.'

'*Please*...' whispered Alexis. It was a thread of a sound.

He was already turning away.

'Come along. I want to check on the frequency of that radio.'

It was a nightmare, Alexis thought. She only had the vaguest idea how the radio worked and the Spaniard who brought her up to speed was as impatient as Michael himself. They left, at a swift march, before she had finished checking. She didn't even have time to kiss Michael or ask him to be careful.

Alexis looked a little wildly at the manual of instructions. It was in Spanish. For a horrid moment, she panicked. Then she thought of Michael. He hadn't had any doubts she could cope. So she *would*.

She applied herself to understanding the controls—which were actually fairly simple—and not thinking about Michael on the treacherous mountain.

What is wrong with me? she thought. I've known him less than a week. All right, last night he drove me crazy. But that could just be physical. And, judging by this morning, it was nothing out of the ordinary for him. He's out of my league and we both know it. He's a stranger. He's completely casual. When Fred arrives he'll go and I'm never going to see him again. So why do I feel like a wife whose husband's gone off into danger?

The answer frightened her so much that she jumped up out of the chair.

'I am not in love with him,' she said aloud. 'I'm immune, aren't I?'

But it didn't stop her hanging over the radio obsessively waiting for the sound of his voice.

At first he gave her nothing more than brief location reports. Alexis noted them carefully on the pad they had given her along with the emergency numbers. Sometimes the reception was so bad that she could have cried. But she didn't. It wouldn't help Michael and if he knew she was panicking it might even make him less careful of his own safety. So she took all the messages in a calm voice and read them back to him without expression.

It got more difficult when they found the couple.

'They're on a ledge,' Michael said. 'The girl seems conscious but dazed. She's not responding to our attempts to hail her anyway. The man looks injured; he doesn't seem to be conscious. They will lower me down from above.'

'Why you?' Alexis said involuntarily.

He didn't seem to hear the anxiety in her voice. She blessed the crackling wave band.

'Because I speak English and that's what these people are. If the girl's in shock, I'll be the best to talk to her.' Did his voice soften or was it an illusion of the radio? 'Wish me luck.'

Alexis was biting the back of her hand so hard that the skin stung. She removed her hand.

'Good luck,' she said quietly.

The next half-hour was terrible. They kept their radios open and she heard everything: every missed footing and overshot rock; every cry of warning and every curse. It was probably a very ordinary mountain rescue, she kept reminding herself. It just sounded so hazardous because she'd never been involved in one before. But her good sense didn't really help.

If only I were *there*, she thought, agonised. Oh, please let Michael be safe.

He came on the radio.

'The girl's all right. Exhausted and in shock but basically she can move. But the man has nasty injuries. I think there's some internal bleeding, though I'm no doctor. We're going to stretcher him up to the shale. Alert the helicopter, will you?'

'Yes, all right. What—what are you doing now?'

'I've strapped him on the stretcher and I'll go up the rock-face at the same time to keep it level and make sure it doesn't bump into the rock,' Michael told her blithely. 'Don't worry about him. This is standard stuff, the boys tell me.'

There was a crackle. The radio went mad. He obviously couldn't hear her. Alexis pushed her headphones back and began to dial the hospital emergency number. Her face was wet.

She said, as if it were a prayer, 'I love you. Come back to me.'

It was a gruelling hour. She talked to Michael. It astonished her how cool and efficient she sounded. Her hands were clammy and her whole body was shaking.

Come home safe. Please, *please* come home safe.

She didn't say it, of course. And Michael sounded sharply efficient, too. Though he wasn't quite so cool. When they loaded the injured couple on to the rescue helicopter he sounded jubilant.

'Be with you in a trice,' he said. 'Good work, partner.'

Alexis broke the connection and sat back, shaking. *Partner*. The trouble was, it felt like truth. And she'd said she loved him, even though he didn't hear. She meant it.

'Oh, good grief,' she said, wrapping her arms round herself and rocking. 'How stupid can you get? If you're too naïve and cold for Patrick, where on earth are you on the Slane scale?'

Well, not cold, she thought, flushing. Or at least it didn't seem to her as if she was cold. Michael might have different standards, of course. And she was certainly naïve.

She must meet him sensibly this evening. No piling into Fred's rioja and flinging herself at his head again. No clutching him to her and weeping with gladness because he was safe. No embarrassing him. Although,

Alexis acknowledged, it was more likely to be she who
was embarrassed. Michael Slane could probably handle
unwanted devotion to admiration. He must have had
years of experience. The thought of him handling her
unwanted devotion was unbearable.

So she flung herself into elaborate preparations for a
celebration meal. It would be sensible if it was also a
farewell meal, she thought. And its object was to keep
maximum food, dishes and tableware between them.
That way he wouldn't take her hand and she wouldn't
beg him to stay with her again.

She applied herself grimly to the task. She had been
chopping vegetables for what seemed like only a few
moments when the kitchen door opened. She looked up,
tensing. Surely it was too soon for the rescue party to
have returned?

It wasn't the rescue party. It was a tall, handsome man
with golden hair and a heavy frown. In fact Alexis had
never seen the patrician features so displeased. She
dropped the knife from suddenly nerveless fingers and
swung round to face him, bracing herself against the
work-bench.

'Patrick!'

He slammed the door shut behind him. She could see
that he was in one of the rages she had come to know.

She said nervously, 'I didn't hear a car.'

'I walked up. There was no one at the garage. Everyone
seems to be up on the mountain.' He spat it out.

Alexis seized the neutral topic gratefully.

'Yes. Some walkers got into trouble. The team went
up after them and they're all right. At least, one of
them's hurt...'

Patrick waved the successful rescue aside impatiently.

'Never mind about that. What the *hell* are you up to?'

Alexis swallowed. There wasn't much sign of the
youthful enthusiast who had taught her all those

summers ago. Or the charming boy she remembered from her childhood. He looked angry and surprisingly mean. Had she really spent eight years of her life in love with this evil-tempered man? she wondered blankly.

'Cooking,' she said.

He took a hasty step forward.

'Don't play games with me. Old Rosa in the bar said you were up here with a man. A *boyfriend*.' His voice was heavy with disgust. 'Is it true?'.

Alexis hesitated. She found she was nervous of him. That was odd because she knew him very well and she hadn't been nervous here alone in the castle with Michael Slane, a stranger. She tried to tell herself she heard the tramp of feet of the returning rescue party.

'I'm very busy. They'll be off the hill in minute...'

It did not convince Patrick any more than it convinced her. He crossed the room impatiently and seized her by the wrists. She winced as he squeezed the injured one. He didn't notice.

'What in God's name do you think you're playing at?' he demanded furiously. 'They say he's some sort of *film star*.' That sounded pretty disgusted too.

Alexis drew herself to her full height and took hold of her courage. Michael had said she was brave, hadn't he?

'Let me go, please, Patrick,' she said with dignity. 'Michael's a good friend and has been very kind to me. He helped when I couldn't drive properly. With my wrist,' she reminded him meaningfully.

That passed him by. 'And he's a celebrity of some sort?'

'A film actor,' she corrected.

He almost flung her away from him. 'An *actor*. My God, you must be out of your mind. You won't let real people touch you, and then you go and fling yourself into bed with some celluloid Romeo.'

Alexis winced. Patrick saw that all right. He paled.

'My God,' he whispered. 'You *have* gone to bed with him.' It was clear that he hadn't really believed his accusation. Now he looked sick. 'I don't believe it.'

A voice from the doorway behind them said softly, 'Believe it.'

Alexis spun round, thinking, They *can't* be here yet. Michael stood there, dirty and dishevelled with a coil of rope over one shoulder. For the first time she noticed the growth of beard darkening his jaw. Of course he hadn't had time to shave this morning, she thought irrelevantly, and he'd been on the mountain for more than seven hours. It made him look tough and supremely physical. And menacing.

The contrast with Patrick's lean elegance was immediate and rather cruel. She saw them both measure each other and make the comparison.

Patrick looked at the torn shirt and dirty jeans and his mouth twisted in distaste.

'Slumming, Alexis?' he asked, not taking his eyes off Michael.

She rushed between them as if they had been about to have a fight. Which was ridiculous, she told herself. They were both civilised men. And anyway, they had nothing to fight over.

'This is Michael Slane,' she said formally. 'Patrick Montague.'

Michael's eyes narrowed. 'I thought it might be. You're Alexis's tutor?'

Patrick said swiftly, 'Friend.' He gave Alexis an intimate look. 'Old friend.'

Michael drew a sharp breath. But all he said was, 'You have an odd way of showing friendship, I hear. So you decided to look up an *old friend*?'

Patrick said coldly, 'Her stepfather suggested I drop in.'

Alexis gasped. Michael sent her a quick look.

Patrick continued smoothly, 'Fred seemed to think she was depressed. She's been off ill, you know. Let herself go rather. Fred thought she'd be better if she wasn't on her own.' Their eyes clashed. 'Do you have any objections?'

Michael shrugged. Through the rents in the disgraceful shirt his tanned shoulders gleamed. 'She's not,' he said levelly. 'Depressed. Or on her own. I'm sure you understand.'

Patrick's hands clenched into fists at his side. But he chose to ignore the implication. Instead he turned to Alexis.

'I know why you're here,' he said in that kindly, patronising tone she knew so well.

All of a sudden she realised that over the last months she had come to dread that tone. Why hadn't she noticed before?

'You thought if you got away you could do something with that piece of nonsense you showed me.' He shook his head sadly. 'Oh, Alexis, my dear, I wish I could show you, you're chasing shadows. You'll only hurt yourself. The Sheldon Prize will go to someone with academic muscle.'

Alexis said in a strangled voice, 'You're wrong. I came because Fred wanted me to.'

But she found she wasn't being attended to.

Michael said mildly, 'Academic muscle like yours?'

It was a gentle enquiry. Patrick didn't seem to see the anger behind it, though to Alexis it was patent.

'Well, I'm a candidate among others,' he agreed complacently.

'You amaze me.' Michael's voice was very soft.

'Oh? Why?' asked Patrick, genuinely puzzled.

'Isn't it unethical to advise a pupil who's also a rival?'

Patrick didn't realise it was an accusation until Alexis drew an audible, shaken breath. He gaped.

'What's it called?' Michael was snapping his fingers, feeling for a phrase. 'Conflict of interest. That's it.' He smiled at Patrick, apparently genuinely interested. 'Doesn't it give you a conflict of interest?'

Patrick's face darkened. Alexis felt as if she'd received a body blow. Nothing could have made it clearer that her love for him had been built on fantasy. And here was Michael, who didn't know anything about the world of classical music or Patrick Montague, getting straight to the heart of the matter.

'You were going in for the Sheldon Prize too?' she said quietly. 'Why didn't you tell me?'

'Because it was irrelevant,' Patrick snapped. 'Anyway, it should have been obvious. A man in my position. Of course I'd go in for it.'

'With all that academic muscle,' Michael murmured.

Patrick looked at him with acute dislike. But he addressed himself to Alexis. 'If you're determined to make a fool of yourself, you won't take me along with you. You'll have to get someone else to sponsor your application. They won't like it, if it isn't your supervisor,' he ended with satisfaction.

Alexis didn't want to believe it. She winced. 'Patrick, that's blackmail,' she said almost pleadingly.

'No, it isn't,' Michael said suddenly. 'It's pure spite.' He turned to her and said in a disbelieving tone, 'Alexis, you really *like* this character?'

Patrick swung round on him. It was all too reminiscent of the day she had broken her wrist. Alexis closed her eyes. The latent violence in him was very close to the surface, she thought, trembling. Michael was watching him with interest.

Patrick said thickly, 'She's mine.'

It was a moment of pure melodrama. Michael gave a crack of laughter. Alexis couldn't really blame him but it still, for some obscure reason, hurt. As if he couldn't imagine anyone laying claim to her, or wanting to lay claim to her. The magic of the previous night slipped sharply into history.

Patrick was obviously infuriated by that cynical laugh. He swung Alexis out of the way and squared up to Michael.

Michael shook his head. 'You don't want to hit me,' he said gently.

Patrick bared his teeth. 'Give me one good reason why not.'

Michael sighed. 'Because I'm bigger and meaner than you. Because I've been street-fighting since I was a kid. Because,' his voice was dry, 'I don't pretend to be a gentleman.'

Patrick swung at him. Alexis gave a little scream. Michael barely seemed to move but he side-stepped and hit Patrick twice, once in the stomach, so that Patrick ran on to the blow with the full force of his own speed, once on the back of the shoulders as Patrick doubled. He let Patrick fall to the floor, gasping.

'Get out,' Michael said in a mild tone. 'And don't come back without an invitation.'

He walked out of the kitchen. Patrick was speechless, bent double. Scared, Alexis went to him. He pushed himself upright, rubbing his face.

'The man's crazy,' he said in a muffled voice. He examined his hands for blood and found none. 'Get your things. I'm not leaving you here with that madman,' he instructed.

Alexis found her alarm disappearing in a rush of anger. She took several steps back.

'Yes, you are,' she contradicted.

He stopped turning his hands over and stared. 'What?'

She thought of what Michael had said: 'You do what you have to.' He'd done all he could for her with Patrick. The rest was up to her.

'You heard what he said, Patrick. Get going.'

He looked stunned. 'But he hit me.'

It was almost laughable, thought Alexis. 'You hit me once,' she reminded him quietly.

He didn't hear it. Or pretended not to. She watched him dispassionately and saw him decide to charm her.

'I can't leave you here with him. Even though you mess me around. I still care about you, darling,' Patrick told her nobly.

Alexis glared at him. 'No, you don't,' she flashed. 'You don't care for anyone but yourself and you never have. Oh, I was easy game at seventeen, wasn't I? Too silly to see beyond the end of my nose and bowled over by a little attention. How on earth can I have let it go on so long? I must have been out of my mind.' She surveyed him unflatteringly. 'You don't even tell your lies well.'

His eyes widened. 'You don't mean that.'

'Yes, I do.' She felt her anger take hold like a forest fire. It was quite exhilarating. 'I thought I'd broken my heart over you, Patrick. But it was nonsense. You don't break your heart over phoneys. You're a phoney, dishonest bully and your wife has my sympathy.'

His face grew ugly. He took a step forward and staggered against the table. Alexis put her hands out instinctively. He brushed her away.

'Get away from me,' he snarled. He hauled himself upright. 'I'm going. Fred's going to hear about this.'

It was such a childish threat that, even in her turmoil, Alexis laughed. It was clearly the last straw. Patrick gave her a look of black hatred and flung out of the door.

She stopped laughing. She shook her head to clear it. She felt disorientated, out of control, cold with shock.

Had Patrick always been like that? Selfish and calculating? No wonder he said she was naïve, Alexis thought with furious self-condemnation. It was there under her nose and she didn't see, she was so blinded by the memory of her adolescent crush.

Not that blinded, she thought suddenly. She hadn't wanted to go to bed with him and it wasn't just because of his wife and children. It was because she must have realised, subconsciously, that he was dishonest through and through.

Whereas Michael Slane—— Alexis stopped dead. How could she ever have thought that Patrick had made her immune? She only had to think of Michael and a small, secret part of her melted. Well, she was out of Michael's league in every way there was, probably, but she'd stake her life that he hadn't lied to her.

And now it was up to her not to lie to him. She went cold at the thought. But there were some things more important than avoiding embarrassment; Alexis knew that now. She squared her shoulders and went to him.

Michael was in his room, pulling off the borrowed walking-boots and socks. He had already discarded his shirt. Alexis could see that there were bruises appearing on the muscled shoulders. Her heart turned over. And Patrick had tried to hit him!

She said in a choked voice, 'Are you all right?'

He looked up. The brown eyes were wintry.

'I'm fine.'

'I'm—I'm sorry about Patrick...'

'Patrick,' he said, without expression. 'Yes. Now why didn't I listen properly when you were talking about him?'

Alexis stopped dead at the icy blast.

'What do you mean?'

'You won't let real people touch you,' he said. She could feel his anger as if he had scrunched it up in a ball and thrown it at her.

Alexis stared. 'What?'

'That's what he said,' Michael reminded her. 'Your Patrick. You wouldn't let real people touch you. By which, I assume, he meant himself. And if he didn't touch you, by your own account, nobody else did.'

Alexis swallowed. He was angry; more than angry.

'You knew that,' she protested in a whisper.

'Hell!' It was an explosion. He ran his hands through his hair, visibly trying to cool his temper. 'I knew you had some interesting inhibitions and a violent boyfriend you needed to get rid of.' His voice was like a whiplash. 'I didn't know you——' He broke off, taking her by the shoulders, his eyes boring into hers. 'Tell me the truth, Alexis. Was last night the first time for you?'

She whitened.

Michael's face stiffened. 'Hell,' he said again.

Alexis wanted to die. Instead she raised her head proudly.

'Does it matter? Why should it? If I don't care——' she swallowed hard '—what business is it of yours?'

His eyes were almost black. He flung her away from him.

'Don't *care* ... It's going to be very much my business if you have my child,' he told her evenly. 'Wouldn't you say?'

Alexis gasped. He had thrown it at her with calculated brutality, as if he wanted to hurt her. She could see that. So it had all been physical and nothing else, after all.

Michael passed a hand over his face. 'Dear God, you really don't understand, do you?' he said wearily.

He took her by the shoulders again. She felt the strength in those muscular arms with a slight shock. Her frame seemed incredibly small and vulnerable in his hands.

'Look,' he said in a harsh voice. 'You set your heart on a fantasy figure for—how long was it? Eight years? When he came back, you didn't like the reality.'

'No,' protested Alexis, but he hardly seemed to hear.

'Then you thought you'd try out your wings with me, God help me. Reality out of the window again.' He shook her, not gently. 'Wake up, Alexis. You can't play with people as if they're toys.'

She was white to the lips. 'I don't——'

'You don't see what's under your nose,' he said harshly. 'While you were breaking your heart and fighting your scruples over Patrick, what do you think he was doing?' For a moment he looked at her as if he hated her, Alexis thought. 'He wants you so badly, he can't see straight.'

Alexis flinched. 'I told him...'

'Oh, God,' said Michael. 'You think that everyone says please and thank you and goes away when they're told to, gentlemen all. Life's not like that. People aren't like that.'

'I know...'

'Oh, but you don't.' He searched her face, his expression grim. 'A man could burn up for you,' he said softly, 'and you wouldn't even smell the cinders.'

'You're crazy,' Alexis said, shaken.

'Am I?' He gave a half-laugh. 'Maybe you're right.'

He pulled her against him so that her hand was caught between their bodies. His skin under her fingers was smooth and tingling with warmth. Alexis gasped. He bent his head so that his mouth was just a breath away from her closed eyelid. She felt his breath, startling as a breeze off the sea, when he spoke.

'Do you ever ask yourself what *I* feel when I touch you?'

'No,' she said. It was heartfelt, involuntary and not an answer to his question.

Michael gave the ghost of a laugh. 'Let me show you,' he said quite gently.

She fell apart. There was no denying it. The change in Michael was too profound, too sudden. After their night of caring passion it was almost unbelievable. Under her horrified eyes, he somehow transformed himself back into the predator she had encountered at Sheila's party.

'Let me go,' Alexis said.

She struggled. But it was too late. He already had her at every disadvantage—off balance, defensive, in his arms. It was all too easy for him to sweep her up and on to the bed, barely acknowledging her resistance.

This time there was no gentleness, no long-drawn-out wooing of her ravished senses. Nor was there any doubt—this time—about his own feelings. His eyes were black with the intensity of them. In spite of everything, it was that intensity that Alexis responded to.

Later, when he had collapsed on top of her, the shame came; and with it the sense of betrayal. Was it only today she had hung over the radio, praying for his safety?

Michael stirred, lifting himself off her. Turning her head, Alexis saw that he looked almost as shocked as she felt. It was no comfort. Today, talking to him on the radio, taking part in the rescue, she had felt as if they were one, saving life—and real, in the same world. It had frightened her a little—she hadn't wanted to embarrass him—but she hadn't felt it was a fantasy, like her feeling for Patrick. She hadn't realised it was going to tear her to pieces either.

And Michael said she used people as toys. Maybe that was what he was used to, even wanted, if it gave him an excuse to walk away and not get involved. What did she know of Hollywood stars after all? She only knew she loved him, Alexis thought desolately.

She hauled herself up on one elbow. 'I think you'd better go,' she said.

He studied her face for a long moment. She saw his eyes scan her—the long, tumbled hair, the faintly trembling mouth, her eyes, her neck... He put out a hand and touched her throat. 'I've marked you,' he said.

Alexis closed her eyes. In every way there is, she thought.

'Just go,' she said. 'Please.'

Still he hesitated. 'I can't... leave you like this.'

Her eyes flew open. Oh, God, was he *sorry* for her? Her temper ignited gratefully.

'Get out,' she said. Her voice rose. She drummed her clenched fists on the crumpled counterpane. 'Don't come near me. I never want to see you again. Do you hear me?' Patrick's insult came back to her. She flung it at him, shouting. 'You—celluloid Romeo.'

Without a word, Michael gathered up his things and went. He banged the door behind him with a force that echoed round the castle.

CHAPTER TEN

ALEXIS lifted her chin, looking round. The big room was crowded with celebrities. Six months ago she had wanted to run from Sheila's party. Now she could hold her own. She smiled faintly. She had that, at least, to thank Michael Slane for. That and a lot of other things, she knew: her confidence, her new-found self-respect, her music...

Above all her music. She had poured all her love for him into her entry for the Sheldon Prize. Just as well he was never going to know. *Serenade for a Toy*, she had called it with private self-mockery. The title was the only thing the judges hadn't liked.

So here she was, cool and confident, circulating in a big reception as if she had never broken two glasses in one evening over Hollywood's hottest property.

She winced, as she always did when she called him to mind unexpectedly. Unlike those nights when she sat in front of the piano and called up his image deliberately, feeling the pain and the terrible, fragile sweetness of it, distilling it into music.

Forget him, she told herself fiercely. Forget him for this evening at least. You owe it to Fred and Sheila.

Her stepfather looked down at her.

'Looks like a good party,' he said with an enjoyment that belied his years. 'Sheila said it would be. Did you see where we were sitting?'

The number of their table was on the invitation.

'You start with the top table and count clockwise,' she said, looking at the black numbers on stalks that stood behind the floral decorations in the centre of each table.

Fred grinned. 'You are so efficient, *liebchen*. Without you I get lost.'

'Without me you'd throw yourself on the mercy of the most glamorous woman in the room,' Alexis said without rancour. She had her suspicions about Fred's interest in Sheila Mallory but so far he wasn't saying anything. She looked at him speculatively.

He laughed. 'Tonight you would qualify for that anyway. I like that dress.'

It was black and simple with a skirt that looked straight until it swirled out into a bloom of handkerchief-frail petals when she turned quickly. It also had a high neckline, no back, and long, loose sleeves like the bell of a flower. Alexis loved it, even though it was more daring than anything else she had ever bought.

Fred said now, 'You are getting more adventurous in your clothes, my dear. It suits you.'

'Not only my clothes,' said Alexis drily.

He nodded. 'Your music also. It is very pleasing.' He hesitated. 'Montague was not the teacher for you. I know you were fond of him——' He paused delicately.

Alexis said nothing.

He sighed. 'To be honest, I didn't care for the family. I know your godmother was good to you when you were little but ... Anyway, it was up to you whom you chose to study with. It was not up to me to interfere. I tried not to. Except once.' He said sadly, 'I told him you were at the castle, I'm afraid.'

Alexis winced. 'So he said. I didn't believe him. Why did you do it, Fred?'

'I thought perhaps if you saw him—if you...' he hesitated '...could get whatever it was out of your system... You see, I thought he was not the man for you either, *liebchen*. But——'

'You were right,' Alexis said swiftly.

Her stepfather's eyes widened. 'Then they're not for Patrick Montague, these tragic serenades of yours?'

Alexis was startled. 'Tragic?'

He was amused. 'Did you think because I was your stepfather I would not hear what is in your music, Alexis? I am a professional too, you know.'

She bit her lip. 'I know. But you're fond of me.'

Fred snorted. 'That doesn't put cotton wool in my ears.' He looked at her curiously. 'Is that why you have never asked me about your work? Because you thought I wasn't impartial?'

'Well, are you?'

'My dear child, I have a reputation,' he reminded her drily. 'I'm not going to risk it promoting second-rate stuff. Of course I would be impartial.' He slanted a look down at her. 'More impartial than Patrick Montague, I gather.'

Alexis bit her lip. 'You might only be in London one month out of four but there's nothing wrong with your information network, is there?'

'It's true, then? You were lucky to find out in time for the deadline.'

Alexis swallowed, her mouth suddenly dry. 'I had it pointed out to me,' she said curtly.

That interested him. 'By Plunkett?'

She was studying composition with Richard Plunkett now.

'No. By—a friend.'

'Ah.' He pursed his lips. 'I would be interested to meet this friend. I think perhaps you owe the Sheldon Prize to him,' he said blandly.

Alexis jumped and stared at him suspiciously. He smiled back, squeezing her hand.

'And next time I don't want to see it first from one of the judges, hmm?'

Alexis laughed suddenly. 'I wouldn't dare,' she assured him.

'Good. Good. And when are you going to tell me about your new commission?' he added with a chuckle.

Alexis stopped dead and rounded on him. 'You are a cunning, conniving old Machiavelli,' she told him roundly. 'How did you find out about that? It was supposed to be secret.'

Fred's whiskery eyebrows rose. 'You thought I wouldn't like your writing a film score?'

She hesitated. 'No, it wasn't that. I—didn't want anyone to know. Or not until I was sure I could do it.'

'Insurance,' Fred said disapprovingly. 'I thought you'd become more of a risk-taker than that, *liebchen*. Perhaps you should consult this inspirational friend of yours again?' He sounded gleeful.

'Fred...' said Alexis on a rising note of sudden alarm.

But he was already turning away.

'Ach, there's Sheila. That must be our table. Come along.'

She followed, frowning faintly. The offer of the film score had come out of the blue. It had troubled her at first. She had every reason to avoid the film world. But it was a low-budget UK production, two characteristics which meant that she was unlikely to bump into Michael Slane in the course of the project. And she really loved the story.

'How is the score going?' Fred asked now, guiding her.

Alexis went with him. 'I've only written four themes so far. That's what they asked for.'

Fred nodded. 'Intriguing. What are they?'

'One's for a crowd scene—a street fight,' she said, ticking them off on her fingers, 'a pastoral, a party theme—though not like this.'

Alexis chuckled, remembering. She had enjoyed writing that, finding rock rhythms and a danceable tune. She had even danced to it herself in the privacy of her studio, allowing herself, for a few seconds in the dark, to remember being held by strong arms and moving to the beat of the human pulse echoed in the music. Even now, she shivered a little at the sensation the memories evoked.

'That's three. What's the other one?'

Alexis bit her lip, her laughter dying. 'The love theme.'

Fred looked at her with a good deal of comprehension. But all he said was, 'Of course. Inevitable. Ah, here we are.'

Sheila Mallory greeted them enthusiastically, though Alexis thought she was looking a little preoccupied. Perhaps one of her clients was up for one of the awards that were being presented tonight.

Alexis had seen Sheila Mallory in Fred's company several times since she'd returned from Spain. She had never once mentioned Michael Slane, and Sheila had never once mentioned him either. Alexis knew that Sheila was now his agent because she had read it in columns of newspapers she would never formerly have seen. But Sheila presumably had no idea of what had followed her party. So there was no reason why she should talk about her new prestige client to Alexis, who was known not even to watch movies.

Though that had changed too. A delighted godson had found that Alexis was more than willing to fill the statutory baby-sitting hours with trips to the cinema or evenings in front of the video-cassette recorder. Henny was too sophisticated to tell his parents the flagrant transgressions of bedtime that were now permitted by his reformed godmother, so nobody knew of Alexis's new preoccupation.

In fact, when Sheila had suggested that she write a film score, Alexis had wondered momentarily if she had been found out. But Sheila had made it clear that her client was looking for a new name with a classical background to bring a fresh approach to the sound. Her lack of knowledge of the cinema was a positive benefit, Sheila had said.

Alexis sat down and began to leaf through the glossy programme she found on her chair. Almost at once she stiffened. Her neighbour looked over her shoulder.

'That's a new award,' he said chattily, seeing the page she was looking at. 'Nice to see some inward investment in the popular stuff. And Slane doesn't do trash, even though he's box office.'

Alexis said in a strangled voice, 'Really?'

She looked accusingly across the table at her step-father. But Fred was deep in conversation, or appeared to be. There had been no hiding from Fred, of course, that she had been living in his house with wild Michael Slane. He had taken it calmly. Tonight was the first time he had shown any curiosity at all in her private life. But he wasn't a fool and he'd be able to deduce the significance to Alexis of that name in the programme. If he hadn't known it already.

She studied him fixedly. Was he avoiding her eye? Had he brought her here deliberately tonight? And if so, why?

Alexis thought with fervour how she never wanted to see wild Michael Slane again. He thought she played games. He was too blind or too callous to see that she'd put her whole heart into loving him. All he'd cared about was the physical experience—and the consequences. Alexis would remember to the day she died his look of fury at the thought that she might be carrying his child.

He'd been honest about it, at least, Alexis reminded herself. Not like Patrick, with his lies and evasions. Michael had never pretended to love her. She'd learned to live with it, even to grow from the experience. But she didn't want to see him again.

She scanned the room for the broad shoulders she never wanted to see again.

Which was why she lost track of the conversation at the table. And didn't hear Sheila's exclamation of pleasure.

'Mickey! You're so late. I thought I'd be accepting the statue for you. You know everyone here, I think. Except perhaps—Alexis?'

Hearing her name, Alexis turned. Her eyes were still searching the crowd. She opened her mouth to make conventional greetings and her eyes locked with Michael Slane's. She stopped dead.

'Alexis, you wanted to meet the producer of *Hunter's Night*. Here he is,' Sheila said, pleased with herself. 'I've shown him your ideas and he *loves* them.'

Alexis was paralysed. There had been no mention of his name on the treatment Sheila had sent her. That had to be deliberate. She searched for something to say and found she had no voice anyway.

Michael's eyes gleamed, as if he could see her discomfort. Which he probably could, she thought, remembering that uncanny perception. She gave him a cool smile. His eyes danced but he nodded to her pleasantly enough.

'We've met,' he said briefly. 'I've listened to your themes, Alexis. Maybe we can get together and talk about them some time,' he added.

He was looking, she thought inconsequentially, much more like a film star tonight. He was wearing a white dinner-jacket which emphasised his tan. The brown hair was styled too, so that the natural waves curled softly against his collar. Alexis felt her mouth go dry.

'No,' she said, her cool evaporating.

Everyone but Michael looked surprised. Sheila appeared faintly shocked. The laughter dying out of his face, Michael's eyes narrowed to chips of granite.

'I can't talk about music,' Alexis said wildly. 'It doesn't work. I don't make sense if I try. If you don't like the themes, Mr Slane, junk them.'

This time it was Fred who looked shocked.

Michael said, drawling, 'Oh, that would be a pity. *Miss Brooke*,' he added, with emphasis.

Sheila looked from one to the other in the alarm of a hostess who saw her guests beginning to get out of hand. A thoughtful expression came over her face. She put a hand on Michael's arm.

'We'd better sit down. The great and the good are lining up,' she said soothingly.

She sat down and tugged at the white sleeve. For a moment it looked as if Michael was going to ignore the silent command and stalk round the table to Alexis. But in the end he obeyed. Though he didn't take his eyes off Alexis.

She saw Fred watching them both in ill disguised amusement. Her temper began to rise. She turned firmly to her next-door neighbour and talked hard.

Food was put in front of Alexis and taken away without her doing more than using her knife and fork to stir it artistically round the plate. Speeches were made, amid laughter and applause, and she didn't catch a word.

Michael got a special award for services to the European film industry which she didn't understand. While he was making his brief, witty speech, Alexis stared down at her hands and prayed that the evening would soon be over. Even across the mighty ballroom and a thousand heads she could feel his eyes on her.

As soon as the music started again, she leaned forward and looked at Fred pleadingly.

'I've got a terrible headache. I really would like to go now.'

'Exercise cures headaches,' Michael said coolly from behind her. 'Come and dance with me.'

Her stepfather smiled at them both impartially. 'Mr Slane. I've looked forward to meeting you. I think you may have been a very good influence on my stepdaughter's work.'

Alexis flushed scarlet and glared at him. Fred was bland as cream.

'Dance with the man, *liebchen*. And bring him to lunch tomorrow. Not too early.'

So no help there. And the implication in her stepfather's worldly amusement was almost unbearable. Alexis had the distinct impression that if she refused Michael would jerk her bodily out of her chair. He could not have been less like the man she had travelled with and squabbled with and played for. And fallen in love with.

Maybe this was the cure, she thought.

Not speaking, she stood up. He pulled the chair back for her courteously. The courtesy was mocking and they both knew it. She flashed him a quick unhappy glance. He caught and held her eyes. Then, very deliberately, he took her hand, folding his own round it possessively. Behind them Alexis could hear the silence at the table as they walked away.

The dance-floor was larger than she expected to find between the crowded tables. But it was tiny in comparison with the main hall of the castle. Michael didn't behave any differently, however. He still took up his stance in front of her as he had at the castle. He put his hands on her waist, holding her a little away from him. He ignored the other dancers as if they weren't there. Alexis could feel the stares like the heat of a spotlight—not just their dinner companions: the whole room seemed to be watching them.

Michael seemed completely unaware, looking only into her eyes.

'Remember?' he asked in a soft voice.

Alexis felt her stomach go into cramp. What the hell was he trying to do? she thought.

'I remember,' she said grimly, setting her teeth. 'I remember *everything*.'

He gave that husky laugh that still haunted her dreams and her music. And one hand slid round to the small of her back.

'Watch my eyes and keep your shoulders parallel to mine,' he murmured. 'I'll drive.'

The music was a strong simple beat. Alexis would have found it easy enough to follow anyway. But she was so angry, she flung herself into the dance with passion.

'Inhibitions definitely on the move,' Michael told her in a congratulatory tone as he whirled her under his arm and plucked her back against his chest in one agile movement. He was laughing—now he'd got his own way, Alexis thought.

She flashed him a venomous look. 'Am I supposed to say thank you?'

He gave her a sweet smile. 'Oh, I don't think it's *all* my influence,' he told her, deliberately misunderstanding. 'You have to take some of the credit yourself. I was impressed by the dance music you delivered. Some real signs of soul there.'

'You wouldn't know soul,' Alexis hissed at him, 'if you met the Archangel Gabriel.'

He shook his head sadly. He twirled her away the length of his arm, and back. Alexis hadn't been expecting it. She choked and had to concentrate on regularising her breathing for a few lively moments. Michael didn't, of course, let her stop dancing.

He smiled down into her indignant face. 'You've got me wrong, you know.'

'I doubt it,' said Alexis when she could speak again. 'You go your own sweet way and the hell with anyone else. And you see what you want to see, regardless of the truth.'

He looked amused. 'What truth do you think I missed, honey?'

She was about to tell him that he hadn't recognised genuine feeling when he'd had it in his grasp. Then she realised where that would lead her. She shut her mouth again rapidly.

'If we're talking fairy-tales, Cinderella,' he said deliberately, 'you were the one who let fantasy run away with her.'

'Don't call me that!' Alexis glared. She didn't really need anyone to tell her that, but it wasn't pleasant to be reminded of it by the man she had set her secret, stupid heart on.

'What did you think you were doing?' he asked in a conversational tone. 'Trying on romance to see if it fitted? Or proving you could get yourself another man if you wanted?' He still looked amused but there was a darker undertone to the husky voice.

Alexis was so angry that she almost hit out. She would have stopped dancing if the iron hand at her back hadn't made her keep moving. 'Come to that, what do you think *you* were doing?' she retorted nastily. 'Proving you could dazzle off-screen too? They told me you and Rosemary Harvey were dynamite on screen. Looking for comparisons, Michael?'

This time it was he who stopped dancing. He stared down at her, an odd expression on his face. He didn't seem insulted, which was disappointing as she'd just said the nastiest thing she could think of. Instead, he looked interested.

'Are you saying you didn't trust me? Ever?'

Alexis tossed back her hair in a flying cloud. 'Of course I didn't,' she said, wanting to hurt him as much as he'd hurt her.

He laughed softly. His hands tightened and they began to dance again. He seemed unaware of the curious stares they were attracting.

'You're a liar,' he said conversationally.

Alexis glared at him. 'How dare you?'

He shook his head. The light danced over the brown-gold waves. Alexis wanted to touch his hair so much that it was like a physical pain. She shut her eyes.

'Think about it,' he advised. 'I told you once. You've got good instincts. You listened to them when you let me into your stepfather's flat that night. You listened to them when you let me drive you to Spain. You know you trusted me really. It's just that you got fogged up along the way because it was all new to you.'

Alexis's eyes flew open.

'If that were true,' she said, ignoring his last remark, 'then I'd say my instincts were in need of a major overhaul.'

He looked down into her eyes with an intensity which all the dancing humour in his face did nothing to disguise.

'Nothing a little tuning up won't handle,' he murmured. His hand moved down her spine in explicit, outrageous illustration.

Alexis felt her heart stop. After a shattering moment, she said with precision, 'If you don't take me back to the table, I'll make a scene.'

Michael's smile grew.

'Good. I could use a little publicity for the new movie.'

She stared at him, balked. 'You really don't give a damn about anyone, do you?'

'Oh, yes.' His smile was crooked. But he still sounded super-cool. 'I give several damns.'

Before she could demand an explanation, the music changed. The new mood was slow, languid. Alexis swallowed hard. There was a definite glint in the brown eyes. He stood still. For a moment she thought he was going to let her go. But then his arms hardened round her.

Alexis was in no doubt of his intentions this time. Anybody watching them—and there were plenty, she realised—would be equally clear. His hands drifted down her body as if they were alone, dancing in the curtained salon again between the shadows of the candles. It was unbearable.

For a moment, in spite of her indignation, her suspicions and even her broken heart, Alexis was moved. She, too, forgot where she was, forgot the others on the crowded dance-floor. She curved back over his arm as Michael bent to set his lips against her throat.

And then there was a blinding flash and she came to her senses. Straightening, she looked over Michael's shoulder, as he turned towards the disturbance. She met the grinning gaze of a man with what looked like the last word in sophisticated cameras. He gave her a cheery wave and pointed the thing at her again. Another flash. Michael said something crisp under his breath. But the photographer was already turning away, pointing his machine at other couples.

Alexis disengaged herself from Michael's loosened grip. She felt icy cold. So that was why he had cornered her. That was why he'd allowed—no, encouraged—her to make a fool of herself on the dance-floor with him. He wanted publicity for *Hunter's Night*. He'd told her the way the film world worked, after all, all those months ago in Spain. She was so angry, she could barely speak.

'Well, that should do your publicity for you,' she said calmly. 'Good gossip-column stuff there, I'd say. Congratulations, Michael. Congratulations and goodbye.' He reached for her arm, not gently. She tore it away. 'Touch me again and I'll slap your head off,' she hissed.

She walked away from him, not waiting to see his reaction or whether he followed.

At their table Fred was on his feet, looking concerned at last. 'Alexis——'

'I'm going home,' she said flatly. 'I'll take a cab.'

She didn't even go to the cloakroom to collect her wrap. She walked out through the hotel lobby without noticing the curious stares. A fatherly commissionaire took one look at her and summoned a taxi.

The cat was waiting for her when she got home. He rubbed his bullet head round her ankles, clearly hoping for largesse, though it was hours past his normal feeding time.

'OK,' Alexis said, hugging him. 'No point in us both going hungry.'

She went to the kitchen and made some coffee while she opened a tin of cat-food. She was restless and wretched. There would be no sleep for her tonight, she thought.

She took the coffee into her sitting-room and sat down at the piano. Running her hands over the keys, she picked out her love theme. She pulled a sheet of manuscript paper towards her. Soon the coffee was cooling and her sore heart was quiet.

She worked through the first grey slivers of dawn. She heard the traffic start in the street. She heard the milk cart—the earliest morning visitor. After that came the paper-boy. She heard the papers land squashily on the mat.

The phone rang. She looked at it with dislike and let it ring. She took the morning papers into the sitting-room and leafed through them idly. Then she turned a page and there was the photograph.

Her first thought was blank disbelief. How on earth could they have had the photograph processed in time to get it into the morning edition of the newspaper? Her second was blank panic. It wasn't on the gossip page. It was among the news. And they had printed her name underneath, with a headline.

ANGLOPHILE MICHAEL SLANE WITH HIS LATEST FLAME.

Alexis looked at the photograph and her skin crawled. She looked abandoned, she thought. Michael was bending over her, his lips at the base of her throat, so his face was in shadow. But there was no mistaking the expression on her cruelly caught face: blind rapture. Alexis shuddered.

She applied herself to the text of the report.

Michael Slane, star of the decade's most successful romantic adventure movies, is moving his operation to the UK. He set up his European production company six months ago. It now has two films in production, co-financed by Slane's private interests and some surprising venture capital. The financiers say they're impressed by Slane's prospectus and so far he's delivered.

Meanwhile, Slane is clearly impressed by gorgeous twenty-five-year-old redhead Alexis Brooke, a new recruit to films, who is working on the score for one of his projects.

They had stopped short, Alexis thought, wincing, of actually saying that no doubt she'd deliver too. But the implication was pretty clear. She found she could quite easily hate Michael Slane.

The phone rang again. She picked it up. A breathless voice she didn't recognise asked her if she was Alexis Brooke and could the caller have an interview about Mickey Slane. Alexis put the phone down without answering.

It happened three more times, with variations, in the next half-hour. In the end, Alexis took the phone off the hook for an hour and went back to work. She covered pages of manuscript paper in a ferocious burst of activity.

She was rocketed out of her absorption by a peremptory rapping on the french window. She looked up. And came to her feet in outrage. It was the hated Michael Slane. He was obviously in a towering temper.

'Go away,' Alexis said in a temper quite as great.

She didn't have much hope of being attended to. He looked tough and dangerous and quite capable of breaking the glass. She glared at him through the window but it was her eyes that fell first. Her nerve broke. She unlocked the door.

He was in at once, slamming the door behind him and turning the key in the lock with a vicious movement that said more clearly than words how angry he was. Alexis backed away.

'Don't you start cowering now,' Michael flung at her. 'I've had more than enough to bear from you, by God. I won't be treated like Attila the Hun on top of all the rest.'

'Then stop behaving like Attila the Hun,' Alexis threw back. 'And it seems to me that *I'm* the one who's had most to bear in this entertaining little exchange of ours. "Gorgeous twenty-five-year-old redhead,"' she mimicked savagely.

Unforgivably Michael looked amused. 'Serves you right for reading the wrong newspapers,' he said. 'And for being gorgeous.'

Alexis looked round for something to throw. The only thing her eye alighted on was her concerto and that was too precious.

'Did you come here to insult me?'

Michael smiled. 'No. To ask you to marry me.'

The concerto was not too precious after all. Several pages flew in different directions but it hit him with a satisfactory thwack on the side of the complacent mouth. He caught most of the flying pages between his hands. He was, Alexis saw, laughing. She was very nearly in tears.

'You've had all the free publicity you're going to get out of me,' she said curtly. 'Go and find someone who enjoys it next time you want to do some hell-raising.'

He said gently, 'But Alexis, sweetheart, I'll never find anyone who enjoys it as much as you do. We were made for each other.'

She met his eyes in disbelief. How could he be so cruel? She turned away. 'Go away,' she said in a muffled voice.

He came up behind her and took her into his arms.

'You are,' he said, exasperated, 'the most contrary, difficult, stubborn and wrong-headed woman I have ever met in my entire life. I adore you.'

His kiss this time was long and illuminating. The cure hadn't worked. Her hands went to her burning cheeks in dismay.

'What are you trying to *do* to me?' she wailed.

'Whatever it takes.'

His grip didn't slacken. Although his eyes were dancing, he looked horribly determined. But determined on *what*?

She spread her hands helplessly.

'I don't understand. Takes to do what?'

'Get you to marry me,' said Michael calmly. 'I told you.'

Alexis searched his face and made a discovery.

'You're serious.'

He laughed aloud at that.

'Don't sound so appalled. It's not good for my ego.'

'But——'

He took both her hands and held them against his chest, looking down at her steadily.

'Listen, Alexis. When I met you, I'd had women to my hairline. They all wanted something out of me—and what they wanted wasn't usually very flattering. Not one of them cared the snap of her fingers about me. And then—suddenly—there was you.'

Alexis stared. 'You said I was experimenting. You said I treated people like toys. You *walked out* on me.'

His hands tightened. 'You said that was what you wanted.'

She shook her head blankly. 'But I didn't mean it.'

'It sounded as if you meant it,' Michael said wryly. 'You'd just had a major encounter with the man you loved. I'd even hit him, for God's sake.'

'But I'd told him to get out. I told him I'd realised I'd never loved him. He was such a sham.'

Michael groaned. 'Why in hell didn't you tell *me*? You looked so wretched, I thought you still loved him.'

Alexis shook her head vigorously. 'No chance. I'd only just realised I loved...' She stopped in confusion.

Michael didn't pretend not to understand. 'You didn't behave as if you loved me,' he said drily. 'Hate more like it.'

Alexis blushed faintly. 'I was scared,' she told the top button of his shirt. 'You—I didn't know anyone like you. And you seemed so—casual. Even when we—by the waterfall. I'd never felt like that before. But you seemed as if you could take it or leave it,' she finished in a rush.

He stared at her. 'Take it or leave it?' he echoed incredulously. 'Honey, I wanted you more than I wanted my first break. More than I wanted to get away from the whole Hollywood circus. More than I've ever wanted anything in my life. It was you—you were living in a soap bubble. You didn't *see*... I was scared. You kept talking about my leaving. And we weren't going to be on our own for long. I had to work fast—and not frighten you off. I nearly went out of my mind.' His mouth crooked. 'I've never worried about frightening girls off before.'

Alexis thought of that brittle arrogance she'd seen, both at Sheila's party and since; and the stark contrast it made to the man she'd fallen in love with in Spain.

'Oh,' she said.

'You forgot the image. Most of the time, anyway,' he said. 'I was walking a tightrope. You seemed to take me absolutely at face value. I'd forgotten what it was like. And then—those eyes.' He touched his thumb very gently under the sooty lashes. 'Every time I looked at you I could see what you were thinking, right through. And feeling.' He raised her hands to his lips and brushed his mouth across the knuckles very tenderly. 'I was in love like a schoolboy before I knew where I was.'

'Oh,' said Alexis, blushing even more furiously. She knew she ought to pull her hands away if she was going to rebuff him. She didn't. 'I don't believe you,' she said hopefully.

Michael gave a short laugh. 'I suppose I can't blame you for that. I was going crazy—wanting you and knowing that you didn't begin to notice. You were like a—a nicely brought-up schoolgirl sometimes. As if you didn't know sex existed.'

'Oh,' said Alexis on a different voice. She removed her hands smartly.

He let her go. She glared at him but he was looking out across the autumnal garden.

'Only—I'm not a schoolboy, Alexis. Sometimes you seemed to want me and then—you didn't seem to have any idea about the signals you were giving out. Do you remember the first night in Spain? You fell asleep on me; made me promise to stay with you. If you hadn't been such an innocent, I'd have pulled the place apart.'

'Oh, lord. I didn't *think*.' She looked at him remorsefully. 'I'm sorry.'

He turned back to her with a shadow of a smile. 'Useful exercise in self-control. Also told me a lot about you. Even if you didn't have the wrong image of me, you had a whole set of crazy ideas about yourself. I knew you needed time. Courting, I suppose. I've never done any courting; I don't know the rules for nice people like you. And we didn't have any time at all, with that jamboree of Fred's hanging over our heads. So I blew it.'

Alexis went and sat down on the sofa. She felt very strange.

'Why do you say that?' she said at last carefully.

'Honey—that last day—you were *afraid* of me. When you told me to get out. Don't deny it.' Michael sounded bleak. He turned back to the garden, his hands in his pockets.

Alexis decided that only the truth would do.

'Yes. But there were reasons for that. You seemed to turn on me. As if you hated me. On top of that terrible day...'

'Because the man you were in love with walked in on us,' he said bitterly.

'*No*,' cried Alexis. 'Because—Michael, will you please come over here and look at me? I can't bare my soul to the back of your head.'

He turned slowly and came to her. This time it was she who took his hands, drawing her down beside her.

'Listen,' she said. 'We'd spent the night together. It was the most wonderful night of my life. And you treated it as if it were—ordinary.'

He began to speak but she put her fingers gently over his mouth.

'No. Let me finish.' She gave a shaky little laugh. 'Before my courage runs out. I couldn't help wondering if—well, if you hadn't wanted to all that much. If it was just physical. If you were just being kind.'

Michael stared at her. 'You're crazy.'

'Well, as you realised, it was all a whole new country for me. And that morning you seemed so *casual* ... I thought, It probably isn't as important to him as it is to me. I've got to be careful not to embarrass him. Can you understand that?'

Michael took her face between his hands and kissed her.

'I haven't met a lot of women who worried about embarrassing me,' he said drily. 'Or not recently. Didn't recognise it. Sorry.'

'That wasn't all. You went up that dreadful mountain. I was in an absolute gibbering dither. I was so *afraid* for you.'

He slipped an arm round her shoulders and drew her against him.

'Oh, sweetheart. I didn't think.'

Alexis said, 'It was all right. You were all right.' She couldn't look at him. 'I told you on the radio link. You didn't hear.'

He said quietly, 'I heard you say, "Come back to me." I was down that mountain like a landslide.'

She sent him a quick, amazed look.

'Then why...?'

'I was sore,' he said swiftly. 'Patrick turned up and there I was kicking him out. You didn't say anything. I thought, Maybe she's just hiding behind me. She still loves him but she knows the relationship's hopeless. So I'm her camouflage. I'd gone out on a limb for you and I didn't even know what you felt. If you felt anything.'

'Is that why you were so hateful?' she asked slowly. 'Shouting at me that I might be pregnant?'

Michael winced. 'No, that was desperation,' he said honestly. 'I knew you were emotionally in a dream world. But it never occurred to me that you hadn't had *some* experience. Stupid, I know. When I realised you'd never been to bed with him and we were facing God knows what consequences after making love I—well, I felt used. The one thing I'd been certain about was that you wouldn't use me. I was ready to kill.'

Alexis shivered. 'I remember.'

Michael let her go. His face looked gaunt. 'Did I blow it, then? Is that why you won't marry me?'

She hesitated. 'Why has it taken you so long to come back?'

'I wanted to.' His voice was very quiet. 'I nearly did once. About three weeks after I left you.' He passed a hand over his eyes. 'But I couldn't. I'd forgotten some magazine interview that Sunday when we took off. So the columnists were digging to find out who I'd been with. There were those photographs of us driving out of the garage. They weren't good, but someone could have tracked you down if they'd tried hard enough. I didn't want to give them any leads to you.' He paused.

'Anyway, I thought you didn't want to see me. I—er—
made enquiries through Sheila.'

'Enquiries?' Alexis echoed.

'If you were pregnant,' he said bluntly.

She flushed.

'They told me you'd changed tutors and were playing
again. Everything was going well for you. While I——'
He gave a harsh laugh. 'I wasn't even sure I still had a
career. Or anything else to offer you. And you'd said
you never wanted to see me again.'

He looked forbidding. But Alexis knew that look and
she was brave, she reminded herself. Michael had said
so. She went to him.

'So what's changed?' she asked, running her lips over
his cheek with little murmurous kisses.

Michael stood very still. She kissed his temple.

His voice warmed into the familiar amusement—
though with that darker undertone that set her nerves
tingling. 'Well, you have a little, I guess—dancing as if
you mean it, writing that music. I told Sheila to offer
you that commission but I didn't think you'd take it.
Or that you'd do it with your whole heart the way you
have.'

Alexis kissed his eyebrow. 'I thought you thought I
was too boring. The way Patrick did. My crazy principles, he called them.'

Michael's hand tangled in the long red hair, tumbled
now from her sleepless night of running her fingers
through it.

'Never boring,' he said with feeling. 'And I just love
your principles. They mean I can afford to trust you.
When I'm in my right mind, that is.'

He turned her round to face him. He was suddenly
very serious.

'Listen, sweetheart,' he said. 'I've never found it easy
to trust people and you've seen what I'm like when I

think I've been let down. I don't know what sort of a husband I'll be. Will you risk it?'

Alexis searched his face. 'Do you love me, Michael?' she said at last. 'Do you really want me?'

His arms went round her so hard that she could hardly breathe.

'I love you. I want you so much, you're never going to doubt it again,' he said. It was like a vow.

Alexis gave a long sigh. She pulled his head down to hers.

'This very smart and expensive dress,' she whispered against his mouth, 'seems to be specifically designed for rapid removal. I will risk marrying you and anything else you care to name.'

At some point the telephone began to ring again. He picked her up and strolled over to the telephone point, disconnecting it one-handed. Alexis hung on to him, laughing.

'If you drop me, I won't marry you,' she said.

He laughed down at her, his face so full of love, she hardly recognised him.

'Then I won't drop you. At least this time.'

He carried her into the bedroom, skirting an ever hopeful feline loiterer.

'Out of the way, pussy-cat,' Michael ordered. 'Things are changing round here.'

Alexis said reproachfully, 'You aren't going to throw Dustbin Dan out in the street?'

Michael dropped her gently on the bed. He went back and closed the door on the cat firmly. He smiled at her.

'No. I'm just adding my name to his on the list of people who know you'll come back to them,' he said softly.

Alexis felt her heart melt. She held out her arms and he came to her.

Accept 4 FREE Romances and 2 FREE gifts

FROM READER SERVICE

An irresistible invitation from Mills & Boon Reader Service. Please accept our offer of 4 free Romances, a CUDDLY TEDDY and a special MYSTERY GIFT... Then, if you choose, go on to enjoy 6 captivating Romances every month for just £1.70 each, postage and packing free. Plus our FREE Newsletter with author news, competitions and much more.

Send the coupon below to:
Reader Service, FREEPOST,
PO Box 236, Croydon,
Surrey CR9 9EL.

- -

NO STAMP REQUIRED

Next Month's Romances

Each month you can choose from a wide variety of romance with Mills & Boon. Below are the new titles to look out for next month, why not ask either Mills & Boon Reader Service or your Newsagent to reserve you a copy of the titles you want to buy — just tick the titles you would like and either post to Reader Service or take it to any Newsagent and ask them to order your books.

Please save me the following titles:	Please tick	√
BREAKING POINT	Emma Darcy	
SUCH DARK MAGIC	Robyn Donald	
AFTER THE BALL	Catherine George	
TWO-TIMING MAN	Roberta Leigh	
HOST OF RICHES	Elizabeth Power	
MASK OF DECEPTION	Sara Wood	
A SOLITARY HEART	Amanda Carpenter	
AFTER THE FIRE	Kay Gregory	
BITTERSWEET YESTERDAYS	Kate Proctor	
YESTERDAY'S PASSION	Catherine O'Connor	
NIGHT OF THE SCORPION	Rosemary Carter	
NO ESCAPING LOVE	Sharon Kendrick	
OUTBACK LEGACY	Elizabeth Duke	
RANSACKED HEART	Jayne Bauling	
STORMY REUNION	Sandra K. Rhoades	
A POINT OF PRIDE	Liz Fielding	

If you would like to order these books in addition to your regular subscription from Mills & Boon Reader Service please send £1.70 per title to: Mills & Boon Reader Service, P.O. Box 236, Croydon, Surrey, CR9 3RU, quote your Subscriber No:...................................... (If applicable) and complete the name and address details below. Alternatively, these books are available from many local Newsagents including W.H.Smith, J.Menzies, Martins and other paperback stockists from 12th March 1993.

Name:...

Address:...

....Post Code:..............................

To Retailer: If you would like to stock M&B books please contact your regular book/magazine wholesaler for details.

You may be mailed with offers from other reputable companies as a result of this application. If you would rather not take advantage of these opportunities please tick box ☐